THE ELECTRIC WATCH REPAIR MANUAL
2nd Edition

By HENRY B. FRIED

C.M.W., C.M.C., F.B.H.I., F.N.A.W.C.C.

B. JADOW & SONS, INC., *Publishers*
New York

CONTENTS
Part 1

Part 2: ELECTRIC WATCH REPAIR
Watches Covered Alphabetically

INTRODUCTION

Electric watches are now an accepted segment of the watch industry. Therefore, the watchmaker is being exposed to them in ever-increasing numbers. This writer was quick to sense the need of supplying instruction in the servicing and repair of these timepieces. He also realized that the watchmaker was unfamiliar with the elements of electricity and electronics. This would cause the watchmaker to shy away from these new timepieces. Therefore, the author undertook to create a basic course of instruction in the elements of electricity and electronics, orienting this with watchmakers' everyday concepts for easier understanding and acceptance.

Thus, the instruction in basic electricity also includes the repair of popular electric clocks and those using transistorized pendulums and balances. In this manner, the watchmaker is led gradually from the most simple electrical ideas to practical electrical-electronic horological applications. The reader will profit most first reading the sections, "A Watchmaker's Guide to Electricity". Then he may begin the expositions on the electric watches in the second section.

This second edition's second section deals mainly with transistorized or contactless tuning fork and balance watches since the electric watch of the earlier period was adequately covered in the first edition. While quartz watches are now with us, the manufacturer officially discourages the outside repair or adjustment of these under their service guarantees; in fact many have sealed cases to ensure such compliance.

The author wishes to thank the many manufacturers of these timepieces for their technical assistance with models and patient instruction to this author.

Henry B. Fried

Part I

A WATCHMAKER'S GUIDE TO ELECTRICITY

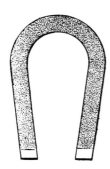

Figure 1. Permanent magnet.

Synchronous electric clocks have been with us for quite some time, and now "cordless," D.C. motor-wound clocks are greatly in evidence. Almost daily, one hears of another energy-cell powered electric watch on the market.

Sooner or later, the watchmaker will be called upon to service these timepieces, all of which operate without mainsprings, the customary winding mechanism, or an escapement. Instead, they use permanent magnets, temporary magnets, electromagnets, wire coils of many types and functions, contacts or switches, relays, diodes, capacitors or condensers, accumulators, resistors, transistors.

The average watchmaker is unfamiliar with these terms; much less does he understand their function. He views these strange timepieces with justifiable apprehension. Actually, these new types of timepieces need not be so fearsome if a study is made of the simple laws of electricity, magnetism and the elements of electronics, terms which seem more foreboding than they really are.

This book is intended as a simple course of study and review of basic electricity as it pertains to timepieces. It should help the watchmaker to better understand and service the new electric or electronic timepieces.

1

Every electric or electronic timepiece is based on magnetic attraction or repulsion. Therefore, we must learn something about magnets. There are three general types of magnetic functions in electric timepieces; permanent, temporary and electromagnet.

A permanent magnet keeps its magnet power almost indefinitely. Figure 1 shows the most familiar form of permanent magnet. However, permanent magnets make take any shape or form, as will be demonstrated later.

TEMPORARY MAGNETS

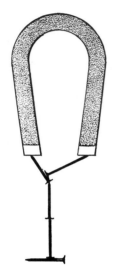

A temporary magnet can be magnetized or attracted by another magnet, and has the properties of a magnet during the influence of any other type of magnet. When this influence is removed, the temporary magnet loses its magnetism. Soft iron and other special alloys have this characteristic. Figure 2 shows a permanent magnet influencing a temporary one in such a way that the temporary magnet has magnetic properties. The permanent magnet attracts pieces of soft iron (in this case cheap iron nails). The nails, now also magnets, attract other nails

Figure 2. Temporary magnets.

and they in turn attract others and so on. When we disconnect the permanent horseshoe magnet from the nails, the nails will no longer act as magnets and no longer attract or support others in magnetic suspension.

ELECTROMAGNETS

Electromagnets exert a magnetic force only when an electric current energizes them. Electromagnets are most often coils of insulated wire or a combination of such wire coils and temporary magnetic material. Almost every watchmaker has basic materials for carrying out simple experiments to help him in this instruction. These are an old-fashioned A.C. demagnetizer, an old file, an old staking punch (or a piece of high-carbon steel rod), a soft piece of iron (or some pieces of soft iron binding wire), a bench compass used to detect magnetism in watches and a piece of clock mainspring.

The demagnetizing coil is used to remove magnetism from watches which have become "permanently" magnetized. This is done by holding the watch or part in the coil and, while current is passing through the coil, drawing out the object in as wide an arc as possible. However, the same coil can be used to make "permanent" magnets of carbon steel objects by placing the steel in the coil, pressing the button to allow current to flow through it and then abruptly shutting off the current (while the object is still within the coil). In almost every instance, the steel piece will become permanently magnetized.

For our experiment, an old file will do nicely, since this is made of high carbon steel and makes a suitable magnet. In fact, some watchmakers purposely magnetize a large file to help them find a small steel part that has fallen off the bench, after which they demagnetize both file and part.

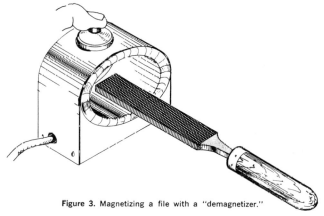

Figure 3. Magnetizing a file with a "demagnetizer."

Magnetize the file by placing its tip in the coil of the "demagnetizer" (as shown in Fig. 3). Press the button for a couple of seconds and then release the current. The result will be a highly magnetized file. If you place this near a high-carbon steel staking punch, it will not only draw the punch to itself but the punch will also become a permanent magnet (although not as strongly magnetized as the file, retaining its magnetism after the file is withdrawn. This proves that steel objects, when brought close to a magnetic field, become permanently magnetized.

CONTROLLED MAGNETISM

In watchmaking, this is not desired, even in the existing electric or electronic timepieces. Since electric timepieces operate on a magnetic push or pull, it is necessary that the magnetic influence end whenever desired. Therefore, a material must be used that can be magnetized temporarily. The most common material that fits these requirements is soft iron. To prove this, we can subject a piece of soft iron to the influence of a permanent magnet and then to an electromagnet. Laminated strips of metal from the stator of an old synchronous electric clock are made of soft iron and can be used for this experiment. If they are not available use cheap iron nails or

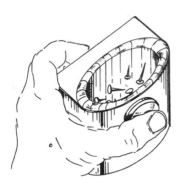

Figure 4. Nails held by current.

pieces of soft iron binding wire. Place a number of these small pieces on the bench and touch one of them with the magnetized file. The iron clings to the file. As you lift the file, the iron piece will hang from it. If you bring the suspended iron piece close to others on the bench, they will be drawn to the suspended piece, in a chain effect: the pieces attracted to the magnet become magnetized themselves, and attract other magnetic materials.

Disengage the iron pieces directly attached to the magnetized file. Immediately, all the other pieces part. Try to pick up some of the pieces with the one that was attached to the file. Unlike the steel punch magnetized earlier, it cannot do this. Should there be some residual magnetism remaining in any of the iron pieces, it is because there may be a small amount of carbon in the iron. However, this experiment proves that some materials can be magnetized only temporarily. In some clocks or electric watches, permanent magnets are not used with temporary magnets—if we were to attract a magnetic balance or a pendulum, it would be necessary to stop this pull as soon as the pendulum or balance neared the magnet, in order that the moving body could return or continue on its own momentum without clinging to the magnet. For this reason, electromagnets are used. These are coils of insulated wire, wrapped around a hollow cylinder of some magnetic substance such as soft iron or an alloy with the same properties.

Your demagnetizer is an electromagnet, and this can be used to demonstrate a useful fact. Put some pieces of iron on the table. Then, place the demagnetizing coils so that the hollow section is directly over the iron pieces. Next, press the button connecting the current. The iron will be drawn into the coil. Lifting the coil while the current is on will cause the iron pieces to cling to the inside of the coil, as shown in Fig. 4. If we suddenly release the contact button, shutting off the current, the nails or iron pieces will drop out of the coil. If we lower the coil, holding it close to the iron pieces, and again press the button, the pieces will be drawn back into the coil and fall back again when the current is shut off.

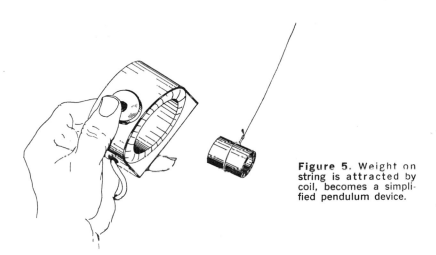

Figure 5. Weight on string is attracted by coil, becomes a simplified pendulum device.

Suppose we put an iron weight on a string, and hold our coil at a spot near the end of this "pendulum's" swing as shown in Figure 5. As the swinging weight nears our coil, we press the button. This will draw the weight nearer the coil. Just as it is about to enter the coil, we shut off the current. The pendulum will swing a bit further on its own momentum and then swing back to the opposite side. When it swings towards the coil again we press the button, and the pendulum will be drawn towards the coil once more; shutting off the current will cause a repetition of all this motion. Thus we have a means of continuing a pendulum in motion. All we need to have an electric pendulum clock is a switch to turn on the current (and shut it off automatically at the right moment) and a counting device to count the swings of the pendulum.

If we placed temporary magnetic tabs on opposite parts of a balance rim, had an electro-magnetic coil to draw these, and an automatic on-off switch, we would have a simple electric watch balance. Such a possibility is shown in Figure 6.

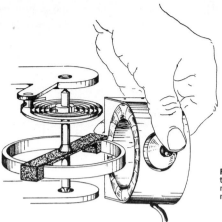

Figure 6. Simple electric watch balance is made by temporary magnets placed on rim.

COMPASSES AND CELLS

Since your demagnetizing coil runs on house current, we cannot operate a timepiece that has to be moved or carried —such as a watch. We will need some source of electrical current that is compact and can be carried with or attached to the timepiece. Of course, we immediately think of the familiar battery. Technically, it should not be called a *battery* but rather, an *energy cell*. When two or more energy cells are are linked together, the combination is called a battery. Therefore, we will hereafter call our compact electrical energy

Figure 7A. Energy cell.   Figure 7B. Battery of cells.

source just what it is—an energy cell. (Figure 7A); unless of course, the cells are formed as a battery as in Figure 7B. We will not now go into the construction of these energy cells or describe the type of current they deliver. However, we should have some additional information on the electromagnetic coil, that wonderful magnetic source that can be turned on and off better and simpler than water from a faucet.

To learn more about this, get a large dry cell and some insulated copper wire such as that used in bell wiring. Next take a piece of old clock mainspring about 6 inches long and

6

shape it to a tapered point at each end, starting outward from its center. With a prick punch, indent (do not pierce) its center so that it can rest, pivot-wise, on a tack or pin sticking through the top of a piece of pithwood (see Figure 8). Then, magnetize this piece of steel in the demagnetizing coil just as

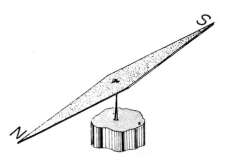

Figure 8. Elementary compass.

you did the file. When you place the poised, magnetized, pointed steel spring on the pivot, you will notice that it will turn back and forth until it finally comes to rest with one end pointing directly north. It now acts as a magnetic compass, and will be very sensitive. This will be a teaching aid in the following lessons and many other interesting and useful things about electricity.

Since one end of this compass points to the north magnetic pole we can mark this end N and its opposite point S. This can be done with a scratch awl or colored lacquer. Generally, the darker point indicates north and the lighter colors, south.

Let us go back to our energy cell. With it we can demonstrate some things about a simple coil of insulated wire, its magnetic power, how this power can be increased, and something about the polarity of an electromagnetic coil.

If a magnet (even our own magnetized file) is suspended as shown in Figure 9, it will act just like our pivoted mainspring strip, and become a directional compass. This is because one end will be attracted to the earth's north magnetic pole and the opposite end to the south magnetic pole. Thus *all* magnets have

Figure 9. Swinging file compass.

polarity. This includes permanent, temporary and electromagnets.

POLARITY IS COMMON TO ALL MAGNETS, BUT IT MUST BE CONTROLLED WHEN PUT TO WORK TO OPERATE WATCHES

We have already shown that both temporary and permanent magnets have polarity. To prove that electromagnets

7

have polarity, we will make our own electro-magnet. By doing so, we can learn some things about one of the most important units of all electric clocks and watches.

Take a piece of insulated bellwire about a foot long. Scrape the ends bare for about a half inch and connect one end to a terminal of a dry cell so that the rest of the wire forms a loop. Next, place the pivoted magnetic compass you have made close to this loop. Grasp the free end of the wire and touch it to the other terminal of the dry cell, making a complete circuit. The compass will swerve (Figure 10), showing that a magnetic force exists close to the wire flowing through it. (Do not allow the wire ends to remain connected to the dry cell; this might drain it.)

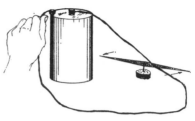

Figure 10

CONCENTRATING MAGNETISM

Let us say that a length of wire a foot long has one "unit" of magnetism per inch. But this is too weak for our purpose; we must strengthen the magnetic field. We can compress the foot of wire and its 12 "units of magnetism" into one inch of space by winding it so that it occupies only one inch. This increases the magnetic force about 12 times. While this is not exactly what occurs, it illustrates our point. We can prove this by winding the wire around a pencil or a piece of pegwood stick so that the coils are very close and compact (the wire must be insulated so that the current does not become short-circuited). Then connect the ends of this wire to the dry cell and move the compass along the coil. In Figure 11, notice how much more pronounced is the magnetic force (near the end of the coil). This proves that a coil of insulated wire concentrates the magnetic field, producing a more powerful magnet.

Figure 11

If we take a long section insulated wire and wind it neatly into many turns and layers, it further concentrates the magnetic qualities of the coil. There is, however, a limit to the number of turns of our coil before we lose the efficiency of the magnetic power, using only one cell.

So far, we have learned that a coil of wire can be made to create a magnetic force. We also found that the more turns to the wire (up to a limit), the greater the concentration of magnetic force. However, much of this magnetic force extends outward, and is wasted in an area where we would rather it did not go; it may even be detrimental. If we could take this straying magnetic force and keep it close to the coil, we would have a more efficient magnet with more influence at the spot we want. We can do this by winding the wire around a soft iron core. We learned earlier that iron "absorbs" magnetism very well. In fact, some of the older watchmakers will remember that pocket watches were sometimes protected from magnetism by placing them in a sheet iron "overcase," called an "insulator." These were black lacquered and lined with velvet. The watch was protected by the casing because the iron absorbed much of the magnetism and provided a circuitous path for the magnetic lines of force around the movement. This kept these lines of force from flowing through the case into the steel parts, as might happen with a case made of brass, gold, or other metals. This property of iron is called *permeability*. Permeability is the ability of a metal to gather in the magnetic lines of force.

We can see this better if we take a magnet and place a piece of clock glass over it in a flat position. Next, place a small needle on top of the glass. As you move the magnet from spot to spot, the needle will follow along on the glass as in Figure 12. This shows that the magnetic lines of force go directly through the glass, just as light would. If you repeat this experiment with a piece of copper or brass instead of glass, the needle will behave in the same way, showing that

Figure 12

these metals, and most others, will allow magnetic lines to pass through them readily. This is why brass makes a good casing for directional compasses; the magnetic lines of force easily pass through it to influence the magnetic needle within.

To understand permeability better, take an unmagnetized needle and place it on the surface of a sheet of iron. The sheet iron that makes up the base of a cheap clock dial will do. Moving the magnet under the iron plate with the needle on it has little influence on the needle. This is because the iron gathers in most of the lines of force. Some of the lines of force from the magnet will pass outward beyond the iron and attract magnetic particles, although in a limited area. Any metal or alloy which has this quality is called "permeable." Iron that is 99.95 per cent pure has a very high permeability, almost 20 times higher than iron that is only 99.91 per cent pure. An alloy often used in electric watches as a core for the electromagnetic is *mumetal,* an alloy of 18 parts iron, 75 parts nickel, 2 parts chromium and 5 parts copper.

To prove that an elctromagnetic coil wound around an iron core has a stronger magnetic force than a hollow coil, rewind the same bell wire around an iron rod or a large nail (Figure 13). Again connect the ends of the wire to the dry cell terminals. Place the pivoted compass near the end of this coil and observe the influence of the coil on the compass, comparing this influence with that exerted previously when the coil was hollow or empty. You will see that the pull is much stronger.

Figure 13

For this reason, electrical timepieces have their coils wound around a highly permeable metal. This strengthens the magnetic force, concentrating it at the desired spots. Also, it may sometimes be necessary (but awkward) to wind a coil in an odd shape to exert this force at one spot. (For example, close to the balance rim, or at a spot between the balance rim and

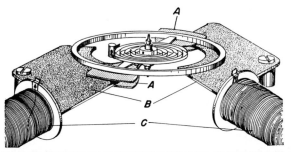

Figure 14. Electromagnet system used in Swiss clocks, similar to the plan in some Swiss electric watches. "A" points to wings made of permeable metal mounted one over the other on the balance, separated sufficiently to allow them to pass over and under the tabs, "B," of the electromagnet coils "C." When balance closes a contact, current surges through the coils.

the main plate as shown in Figure 14.) To obtain the same result, the electromagnetic coil may be wound around this metal or alloy, leaving some of the metal extending beyond the ends of the coil. This may then be shaped in any manner by stamping. Again, remember that permeable metals and alloys do not retain their magnetism once the magnetic influence is removed. This makes them ideal partners for the electromagnetic coil, which exerts its force only when a current is flowing through it and thus, with a switch, can be turned on and off.

POLARITY

If an electromagnet is connected to the terminals of a dry cell, one end of the coil will attract only the north pole of our pivoted compass while the other end of the coil will attract only the south pole opposite. In other words, the electromagnet has a definite polarity, depending on the direction the current flows through the turns of wire. When we connect one lead of the coil to the plus (+) terminal of the cell, and the opposite lead to the minus (—) terminal, the end of the coil which is connected to the plus terminal will point to the north magnetic pole (if the coils are wound in a clockwise direction). The end of the coil which terminates at the minus post (terminal) of the cell will point to the south magnetic pole (see Figure 15). Notice that on dry cells, also called energy cells, the plus terminal is usually in the center, the minus terminal at the side. In the flashlight type dry cell, the plus terminal is situated at the top, and generally has a slight button or head, while the bottom contact is the minus terminal. The plus terminal is also called *positive;* the minus terminal is also called the *negative.* Some of these types of dry cells (ener-

Figure 15

gy cells) are illustrated in Figure 16. Notice that some of them have the plus terminal on the base.

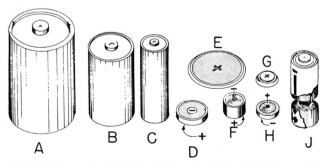

Figure 16. Energy cells. "A," "B" and "C" are the familiar flashlight types. "D" is used in the Swiss electric watch. "E" is the Leclanche cell used in some Swiss models. "F" is the energy cell used by Timex. "G" is used by Bulova, "H" by Hamilton. "J" is actually a battery of three energy cells, unsuitable for watches but widely used in compact hearing aids.

A knowledge of polarity is important in the study of electric watches because in certain watches (such as the Hamilton, Timex, Epperlin, etc.) the electromagnet is wound, and contacts are plotted in such a way that they have a definite and purposeful polarity. If it were possible to reverse the energy cell leads and connections, these watches would not operate correctly. But to study the reasons why this is important, we must learn some additional facts about magnetism.

As we understand now, magnets of all types have polarity. One end is a south magnetic pole and the other is a north magnetic pole. If we place two magnets together, they either become strongly attracted to one another or else repel one another. If we place the south pole of our magnetized file near the north pole of our pivoted compass, the compass point will quickly and strongly swing towards the file tip. If we place the same file end close to the south pole end of our compass, the compass will swing away from our file. In fact, you can discover which end of your magnetized file is the north pole by placing it adjacent to the pivoted compass and observing which end of the compass is either attracted to the file or repelled by it. From this fact we can establish that like poles attract and unlike poles repel each other. These attracting and repelling properties exist in an electromagnet with current or a permeable magnet under the influence of a magnet of any other type.

LINES OF FORCE

The "magnetic lines of force" emanating from an electromagnet or a permanent magnet arrange themselves in a definite pattern. We call them "lines of force" because we can "see" them. From numerous experiments, scientists have observed that when small iron filings are sprinkled near magnets, they arrange themselves in a definite pattern. We can easily observe this, and learn a great deal about the magnetic attraction and repulsion of magnets when they pull or push a balance, pendulum or tuning fork in certain timepieces.

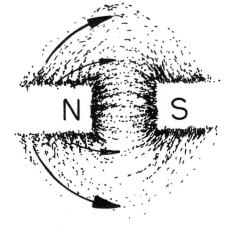

Figure 17

Magnetize another file, and from the pivoted compass, discover the polarity at each end and mark it accordingly with the north and south poles. Next, place both files end to end so the poles are of opposite polarity, separated by about three-quarters of an inch. Place a sheet of white paper over the files. Then sprinkle some iron filings from a piece of soft iron over the paper near the junction of both files. The filings will arrange themselves in a pattern (see Figure 17), and thus we can surmise that magnetism exists in lines of force. The area which these lines covers as shown by the filings is called the "magnetic field."

Lift the paper from the magnets an pour the filings into a bottle so they can be used again. Reverse one file so that its end, say the south pole, is opposite the south pole of the other magnet—but again separated by about 3/4 of an inch. Cover the files with paper and sprinkle iron filings over the junction. The filings will arrange themselves over the magnetic lines of force, but they will appear as in Figure 18, because the lines of force from the similar ends repel one another. Notice also that the strongest concentration of the magnetic field is at the ends of

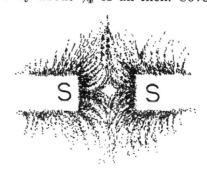

Figure 18

the magnets. As indicated in Figure 17, we see that the magnetic lines of force travel from north to south.

SHAPES OF MAGNETS

If we break a bar magnet in two, the broken ends will assume polarities opposite from their original ends. For example, suppose we have a bar magnet with a north pole at the right. We then break this in two. The original ends will remain unchanged, but the broken end of the magnet at the left will become a south pole and the broken end at the right will assume a north polarity. If we continue to break or divide these sections, we will obtain the same results (Figure 19). Eventually, the bar or rod magnet would become little more than strips or discs. However, in such a process, it is possible for the top to have the opposite polarity from the surface below.

Of course, these can be polarized in much simpler manner, but this should explain

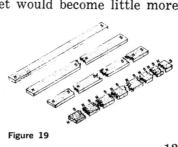

Figure 19

13

that magnets can be made to any shape and polarity. Thin magnets with polarities opposite one another are used in the Hamilton-type electric watch. In some electric pendulum clocks, the pendulum is made of an electromagnetic coil moving within a curved bar magnet with the same polarity at extreme ends while the center has a polarity opposite to its ends.

Electromagnets also have polarity. When a length of wire is wound in a cylindrical coil, one end will be a south pole and the other end a north pole. Furthermore, this polarity can be planned so that the ends have the polarity desired. The wire lead attached to the plus end of the cell and wound in a *clockwise* direction will have at this end a north magnetic pole, and the opposite end will become a south magnetic pole (see Figure 15). Should we compress this coil so that it forms a coil like that in Figure 20, or even one like Figure 21, its polarity would be north on top and south below, as shown in the drawing. Therefore, it is possible to have flat, permanent

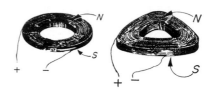

Figures 20 (left) and 21. No matter what its shape, a disc formed from a compressed coil will have the same polarity as the original coil.

magnets with top and bottom opposition and equally flat electromagnets with north and south situated as the heads and tails of a coin.

If we can make such a flat magnet (coil), it can be mounted on a balance (as in the Timex, Hamilton, etc.), and either a permeable material or a permanent magnet can be situated in the narrow space below and/or above the balance at such a spot that brings about the greatest magnetic efficiency on the balance motion when a "switch" turns the energy cell current on and off.

A CURRENT of electricity can be likened to water flowing through a pipe. But electricity flows through solid wires. It has pressure, rate of flow and, just as there is friction in water-pipes, there is resistance to the flow of electricity. At times, this resistance is deliberately planned.

Electrical current can be made to flow from an electric cell (another term for dry cell, energy cell or battery). The electric cell was the invention of Allesandro Volta (1745-1825), a contemporary of Breguet. Volta made a cell by immersing a strip of copper and a strip of zinc in acid. He then attached a wire to each of these metal strips, and by touching one wire to the other, created an electrical spark. Volta also introduced the

idea of connecting **cells** together to form a **battery.** Actually. if we take two strips of
unlike metals and immerse
them in a dish of water, we
create a potential śource of
electrical energy.

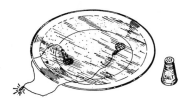

To illustrate this, connect an
electrical wire clip to a copper
penny and another such clip to
a piece of zinc. Immerse them

Figure 22. Simple electric cell.

in water and add a bit of table salt. Touching the ends of these
leads to the proper parts of a tiny light blub will cause it to
glow faintly, as shown in Figure 22.

"DRY CELLS"

However, since it would be awkward to use an electrical cell
requiring a liquid caustic agent or acid as an "electrolyte," a
more convenient form of "dry" cell is employed. But even this
is not really dry. It contains a moist paste of ammonium
chloride (sal ammoniac) and manganese dioxide. The container
is made of zinc, and forms one electrode, while a carbon rod
in the center serves as the other electrode. There are many
other compositions which can be used to create a source of
electrical energy. Wrist watches and other small devices requiring a compact source of energy use different materials
to make up an energy cell or battery of cells, among which
are the mercury type of energy cells. The compact, button
"dry" cells are designed to supply a flow of electrical pressure (volts) in small quantities over a long period of time.
This type of cell can be likened to a water pistol that squirts
a stream, although a very thin one. In this case, while the
stream has some power, the actual volume of water is negligible.

Some types of electric cells can be renewed by recharging
—e.g., the storage battery in an automobile. These operate by
a combination of two rods of lead immersed in a solution of
dilute sulphuric acid. If the rods are connected to a source of
direct current for some minutes, bubbles form around each
rod (electrode). A brown coating forms on one of the rods
(the positive pole). Oxygen forms at the positive plate, changing the lead to lead dioxide. Hydrogen is freed from the
negative plate, which is reduced to a spongy form of lead.
When this occurs, the cell is *charged.* This is shown in Figure
23.

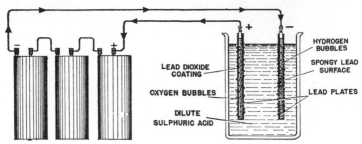

Figure 23. When a storage battery (like one used in an automobile) is charged, lead oxide and oxygen form on the positive electrode. Hydrogen, when freed from the negative electrode, changes the surface to a spongy form of lead.

In Figure 24, wires are connected to the rods and also to the terminals of a bell or a small light bulb. The bell will ring or the bulb will become incandescent for awhile; then the bell stops ringing or the light goes out. The cell has now become discharged. The rod electrodes will look just as they did before being charged. The cell can be recharged by repeating the original charging process.

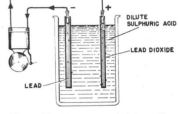

Figure 24. When connected for a time to a bell or small light bulb, a cell will "run down," or become discharged. The electrodes will then appear as they did before the charging process.

In a watch, such a cell can be shaped to fit in the back of the case. It can be recharged by connecting the terminals to another form of dry cell which will recharge it. Such a cell, shown in Figure 16-E, is in the watch being recharged by another, larger cell shown in Figure 25.

MORE ABOUT VOLTS

Generally, most cells supply 1½ volts of current. But what is a volt?

The volt is to electricity as pounds (pressure) per square inch is to a water supply. Each electric cell, regardless of size, is analogous to a shallow tank of water with a spigot at its base. A larger cell is like a larger tank with the same water level as the small one. It will hold more water, and thus last longer, but the stream of water that will emerge from the spigot will be the same. (See Figure 26.)

Figure 25. Charging a watch cell.

16

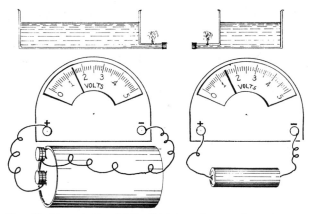

Figure 26. A large electric cell (left) will last longer than a smaller one because it has more "stored up energy." But it won't put out any more volts.

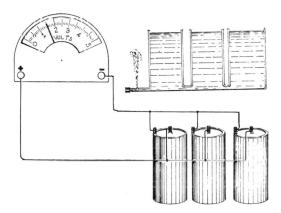

Figure 27. A battery of cells wired "in parallel" will last longer than a single cell, but the voltage will not increase.

If we connect two or more cells to form a battery, but with the leads in parallel (Figure 27), the battery will last longer than the cells would have separately, but the electrical pressure or voltage will remain the same as that produced by a single cell. Here, all of the negative (—) leads are connected to one another while the positive (+) leads are joined to one another. Such a hook-up is called "in parallel." This can be compared to a number of water tanks connected on the same level or parallel to each other, as shown in this same figure. The effect is the same in the larger water tank but with the same level of water.

Should we arrange the same tanks so that each tank's pressure is added to the other, the water pressure coming out of one one spigot will be equal to the *sum* of the pressure of each individual tank (the weight of each column of water is added to the one below it). This is shown in Figure 28.

We can do the same thing with electric cells. If we connect the positive lead from one cell to the negative lead of an adjacent cell, and so on, we get the voltage (pressure) of all the cells thus connected $(1\frac{1}{2}+1\frac{1}{2}+1\frac{1}{2})$, or $4\frac{1}{2}$ volts. This procedure is called "connected in series." When we continue this process, we will obtain the combined pressure of all the cells. Thus, it is pos-

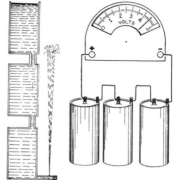

Figure 28. If connected "in series," electric cells form a battery that will produce the combined voltage of all the cells.

sible to get a desired voltage by hooking up electric cells in series, as shown in Figure 28. The cells pictured in Figure 27 are connected in parallel. (Note: most cells, regardless of size are rated at $1\frac{1}{2}$ volts.)

The Lip electric watch uses two $1\frac{1}{2}$-volt cells (Figure 29), in parallel instead of in series. This does not increase voltage, but permits the watch to run longer between power cell changes.

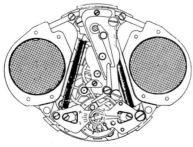

Figure 29. Two parallel cells are used to power the Lip electric watch.

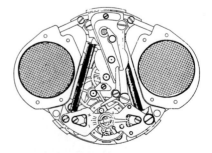

Figure 29. The Lip electric watch operates on two connected coils of wire totaling 10,000 turns.

Our comparison of an electric circuit to a water supply system does not end with pressure or voltage. In a water supply system a pipe with a large inside diameter will permit more water to flow from the reservoir in a given time than if the pipe were smaller. In electricity, the same holds true. If we use a thicker wire, more electricity will flow from the source and, like the water tank, the supply will be exhausted sooner. If we increase the pressure on the water, more gallons will flow in one minute. Likewise, if we increase the thickness of our wires, we get more electricity; if we have a battery of cells, more electrical pressure (voltage) will deliver more electricity "per second." This electrical current flow is called "amperage."

A flow of water is measured in gallons per second. This unit defines quantity as a standard interval. In electricity we also measure the quantity of electricity that passes in one second. A unit of electricity is called *coulomb* (6.28 billion billion electrons). If this passes through the wires in one second, the current is one *ampere*. This is measured with an *ammeter*.

Resistance to a current of water can be caused by friction in the pipes, the length of the pipes from the supply to the outlet, the smoothness of the bore and other factors. Thin piping offers greater resistance to the passage of water than thicker tubing, as shown in *A* of Figure 30. Here, the thicker opening of the short tubing at the right allows more volume to pass than the longer, thinner tubing at the left. Likewise, as shown in *B* and *C* of the same figure, in an electrical circuit, a very long, thin wire offers greater resistance to the passage of electricity than a shorter, thicker one. Thinner wire resists electrical flow more than does thicker wire. This is shown by the ammeter readings of the long thin wire, *B*, as compared to the short, thicker wire, *C*, in Figure 30.

Not only do the thickness and the length of the wire affect the flow of current, but so does the composition of the metal. Some metals conduct electricity better than others. Silver is the best conductor of electricity; that is why some contacts have silver tips. Next in order of superiority of electrical conduction are copper, gold, aluminum, zinc, tungsten, brass,

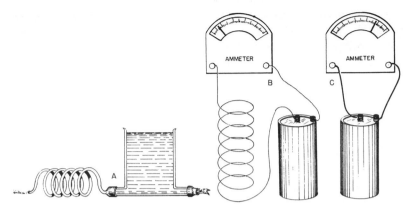

Figure 30. Just as the long, thin tube on the tank, "A," allows less water to pass than the short, thick tube, the long, thin wire, "B," allows less electrical voltage to pass from the cell than does the short, thick wire in "C."

tin, iron, nickel, platinum, soft steel, mercury and cast iron. Because silver is expensive, copper, being next best, is used most often. Carbon is also a conductor of electricity.

Conversely, some materials resist the flow of electricity. These materials are called *non-conductors*. Because they resist the flow of current, they are used as insulators. Some of these are: dry air, shellac, paraffin, ebonite, porcelain, rubber, glass, mica, silk, paper, wood, slate, celluloid, distilled water (not tap water) and alcohol. Because they conduct practically no electricity, these are used to separate adjacent electrical conductors, such as one turn of wire from another in a wire coil, or for the cover of electrical wires, condensor plates, etc.

We have learned that a comparison of water and electrical current shows that we measure water in quantity in gallons; electricity in *coulombs*. Water pressure is measured in pound per square inch; while electrical pressure is measured in *volts*. The flow of a current of water is measured in gallons per second. In electricity, this flow is measured in *amperes*.

One gauge peculiar to electricity is the resistance or impedance to a current. This resistance is measured in *ohms*. The knowledge of the nature or measure of a resistance to an electrical current is of great importance and assistance to a watchmaker who works on electric watches or clocks.

OHM'S LAW

Ohm's Law is a simple formula that anyone can learn. It requires only elementary math. With it you can gauge the amperes, volts and ohms of any electrical circuit or device. With this knowledge you can detect flaws in the electrical circuit, coils, contacts and general efficiency of a watch or clock.

FIGURE 31 — OHM'S LAW MAY BE EXPRESSED IN THREE WAYS

IN TERMS OF:	MEASURED IN:		FORMULA EXPLAINED:	SIMPLIFIED FORMULA:
CURRENT	AMPERES	=	PRESSURE (VOLTS) / RESISTANCE (OHMS)	AMPS = $\frac{VOLTS}{OHMS}$
RESISTANCE TO FLOW OF ELECTRICITY	OHMS	=	PRESSURE (VOLTS) / CURRENT (AMPERES)	OHMS = $\frac{VOLTS}{AMPS}$
ELECTRICAL PRESSURE	VOLTS	=	CURRENT (AMPERES) X RESISTANCE (OHMS)	VOLTS = AMPS X OHMS

Figure 31. A simplified explanation of Ohm's Law. In electrical terminology, the symbol for volts is "E." Amperes is expressed as "I" and ohms as "R." Standard electrical formulae, such as E=IR and its variations, were omitted for simplicity.

Figure 31 shows us that knowing any of the two values, we can obtain the third.

For example, we have a problem deciding how large a current a single cell (1½ volts) will send through a wire with a resistance of 300 ohms. It is solved easily:

Amps = Volts divided by the resistance (300 ohms). In simpler form, $\frac{1.5}{300}$ = .005 or five thousandths of one ampere, also termed five *milliamperes* (thousandths of an ampere).

PRACTICAL APPLICATION

Now let's apply this knowledge to the repair and adjustment of an electric watch. The French (Lip) electric watch operates on two connected coils of wire (Figure 29), each containing 5000 turns. From the stated current of six microamperes (six millionths of an ampere or .000006) under a voltage of 1.50 volts, we can find the proper resistance value of the coils.

With a sensitive ohmmeter, we can test whether the coil is defective. Using our formula Ohms = Volts/Amps we substitute our known value or 1.5/.000006 = 250,000 ohms. Should our meter read much less than that number, we can assume that a short exists in the coils. In Figure 32, such a device is shown testing the coil efficiency of a Hamilton electric watch.

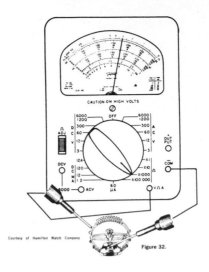

Courtesy of Hamilton Watch Company

Figure 32.

WIRE RESISTANCE

The resistance of a piece of metal wire depends not only on the type of metal used for the wire, but also on its length, thickness and temperature.

The longer the wire, the greater resistance. Suppose a length of wire 100 feet long has a resistance of one ohm; the same wire 100,000 feet long would then have a resistance of 1000 ohms. If the same length of wire was substituted for one with a cross section of half the area, the resistance would be doubled, and this wire would have a resistance of 2000 ohms.

For example, let us take again the Lip electric watch with its coils totaling 10,000 turns of wire. The thickness of the wire is .025mm. Since we know the resistance of the coils to be 250,000 ohms, we can divide the 10,000 turns into the 250,000 ohms resistance and find that the wire has a resistance of 25 ohms per turn (approximately — because the inner turns are shorter than the outer layers of wire).

TEST QUESTION

If the Hamilton electric watch has a stated 3100 ohm resistance in its coil, and uses a 1½ volt cell, what is the amperage?

UNDERSTANDING ELECTRIC METERS

Since we are going to use electric meters while testing clocks and watches in our work, we should know the basic principles of their construction and operation.

Electric meters are comparatively expensive. A working knowledge of their construction and principles is necessary to interpret their readings properly, and to avoid "burning out" their delicate mechanisms.

In some ways, the action of a meter is similar to the circuitry of some electric timepieces.

In a meter the indicator hand is impulsed electrically and turns in a pivoted arc. The hand is poised like a balance, has hairsprings which resist an impulse, and then help return it to the zero position. The pointer pivots on jeweled bearings.

THE GALVANOMETER

The galvanometer is a simple, but sensitive, instrument used to make comparisons between quantities of electric current. Voltmeters and ammeters are basically galvanometers—but with some additions.

We can demonstrate the principle of an electric meter with a simple experiment. First, wind a coil of about 25 turns of fine wire around a hollow paper core, so that the coil will fit loosely between the prongs of a horseshoe magnet. Arrange the coil so that its rounded surface is adjacent to the prongs of the magnet, as shown in Figure 33, and suspend it loosely

Figure 33

in this position. Connect the ends of the coil to an electric cell for a moment. Watch the action of the coil within the prongs of the magnet. Note that when you complete the electrical circuit by touching the wire to the cell lead, the coil twists to some degree.

Now reverse the leads and observe the action. The twisting motion reverses itself. Should you double the voltage by hooking up additional cells in series, the twisting action of the suspended coil will be more pronounced.

The action of the coil within the magnet is principally that of a simple galvanometer. Earlier we learned that when a current is sent through a coil of wire an electromagnetic force is created. This force has the same characteristics as a magnet, including polarity.

Thus, when a current was sent through the small coil, it assumed the properties of a magnet and its poles attempted to align with those of the permanent magnet. It did this by twisting to approach the opposite poles of the horseshoe magnet, and was simultaneously repelled by the magnet's similar poles. The degree of twisting depends on the strength of the electromagnetic force created by the electric cell or cells.

If we could mount an indicator hand on the twisting coil and arrange some scale or dial, we would have a simple means of comparing different electrical values.

In effect, we would have a simple galvanometer.

Figure 34 shows a simple horseshoe magnet. A "split-ring" magnet may be used as well. Fasten the magnet to a housing. The magnetic field supplied by this magnet has a fixed polarity. The lines of force are represented by dotted lines.

Figure 34

Figure 35 indicates that a soft iron core has been mounted in a stationary position between two soft iron pieces attached to the prongs of the magnet. Their purpose is to concentrate the lines of magnetic force. Earlier we learned that soft iron has this ability.

Figure 35

In Figure 36, the core piece of cylindrical soft iron and the soft iron attachments cause the lines of magnetic force to become radial, like the spokes of a wheel, and flow from the north to the south pole.

Figure 36

Instead of the round coil used in our experiment as shown earlier in Figure 33, a square type of coil is wound on a form and held by an adhesive or shellac (Figure 37). The square form will closely fit around the core of soft iron, since the profile of a cylinder is rectangular or square. Most coils are either wound around a paper form, or the coils are their own form, held together with shellac.

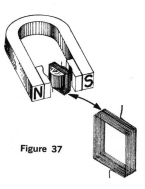

Figure 37

The coil is intentionally light and delicate so that it responds quickly and easily to electrical stimulus, although its delicate construction makes it susceptible to damage. When the two ends of the box-like coil are attached to a source of electric current, the current produces a magnetic field of its own. (The coils are pictured in this position for clarity only.)

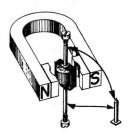

Figure 38

In Figure 38 two pivots have been attached, one above the coil and the other on line below it. The pivots are attached to the surface of the coil by shellac, or a similar substance. The pivots are carried by two cup-jewel bear-

Figure 39

To combine the elements of a meter we start with a horseshoe magnet (Figure 34), add a soft iron core (Figure 35) which causes the lines of magnetic force to become radial (Figure 36); add a delicate coil (Figure 37), two pivots (Figure 38), and two hairsprings (Figure 39) to restrain the coil.

ings, much like the pivots of a clock. The cups are usually sapphires. This permits the coil, when in circuit and containing a flow of current, to attempt magnetic alignment with the permanent magnet.

The alignment of the coil's field with that of the permanent magnet is restrained by two hairsprings, as shown in Figure 39, situated on each shaft of the pivot.

The springs also carry the current to be measured in and out of the coil. The two hairsprings serve as a restraining force —they return the coil to the zero position after the electrical stimulus has been removed. The ends of the box-coil are attached to the hairsprings and carry the current to be metered to the coil. The hairspring ends are generally soldered to the terminals on the meter casing.

Now that we have the elements of an electric meter, we must place an indicator-hand on the upper pivot-shaft, as shown in Figure 40. This hand is usually made of aluminum or other light alloy to maintain the sensitivity of the coil and in case of an over-charge in the meter, are not so heavy or rigid as to cause the pivot to be dislodged from the coil.

Notice that the hand-indicator is poised. Poising is effected by winding a short length of wire around the tail of the indicator. Sliding the little wire along the indicator's tail alters the poise. Sometimes the tail itself is bent up, down or sideways to achieve a precise adjustment.

Under the indicator-hand a scale is placed, calibrated to the meter and its task. Banking pins prevent excessive angular motion of the indicator.

So far we have pictorially constructed a simple electric meter. A cursory study of the coil and its hairsprings shows that if the meter were subjected to large currents of electricity, the coils, springs and connections would melt from the excessive heat. Do not use a meter without first understanding how it operates and its limitations. Every electrical device, whether a toaster or an electric watch, carries a definite current. Subjecting it to current beyond its limit will destroy it; often an expensive loss.

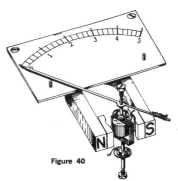

Figure 40

For example, a flashlight uses two cells in series (three volts). The resistance of the filament in the little bulb is six ohms.

Using Ohm's Law, we find that the flashlight will use .5 amperes. The bulb's filament will burn white hot, producing a beam of light. Should we use this bulb on a four-cell flashlight the amperes will double, causing the filament to melt and burn out. Conversely, using the bulb with a one-cell flashlight will permit the filament to become only red hot, not bright enough to produce the desired beam of light.

The Ammeter

We said before that ammeters and voltmeters are basically galvanometers, but with specific variations.

If we take a galvanometer and place a piece of wire across the leads, it would register less than it would without the wire. The galvanometer can be likened to a water meter where *all* the water must go through the meter.

Add a by-pass to this water meter, as shown in Figure 41, and this same meter can handle larger quantities and greater water pressure.

To do this, a small portion of the water going through the pipe is diverted by the same pressure that moves the main stream. This small stream motivates a meter which records the comparative amount of the small stream. Since the same pressure is moving both streams, the gauge's dial can be calibrated to reflect the actual quantity of the entire stream.

In this way only a small amount of water need be sent through the meter at one time, and it can be used to gauge many different degrees of water pressure. All you have to do is change the size of the shunting pipes and vary the dial markings.

Similarly, the galvanometer can be designed to indicate amperes or volts. For the ammeter a shunt is used as pictured in Figure 42. While most of the current goes through the shunt, a small but comparative amount goes through the meter, to register on an appropriate scale.

The quantity of current going through wires *A* and *B* is in direct multiple proportion to the current going through the meter at *C*. Thus when the meter is supplied with a series of shunts it reads the value in amperes.

It is possible then for one meter, supplied with a multiple switch which connects with shunts of different values, to be able to gauge many ranges.

The Voltmeter

A coil of wire resists the flow of electricity like a hose resists the passage of water. The force of a current of electricity, expressed as volts, is measured by the voltmeter. Once again, too much voltage will burn out the coil and hairsprings. Just as the shunts diverted the main flow of current in the ammeter, a resistance is used to measure comparative pressures of electricity with the voltmeter.

THE AMMETER

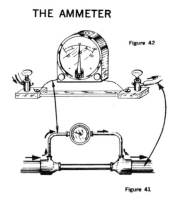

Figure 42

Figure 41

Unlike the ammeter, which is connected in parallel as illustrated in Figure 42, the voltmeter must take the direct force of the current because the connections are in series.

To gauge this force without destroying the meter, a resistance is placed between the gauge's terminals and the source of current. A form of voltmeter is shown in Figure 43.

To measure the voltage of a cell, the meter's leads are attached across the leads of the cell. Do not, of course, use a meter with a limit less than the potential of the cell or battery.

Water doesn't flow directly through the gauge to measure pressure. The gauge only judges the pressure through the pipes. With a voltmeter, practically no current passes through the meter. The meter merely gauges the electric pressure. The resistance coil limits the flow of electricity through the meter.

Suppose a meter has a dial with a maximum reading of 30 volts. Should we attach a coil which resists the flow of electricity by five times, the 30 volt reading can be transcribed to read 150 volts without harming the meter.

By connecting a coil which decreases the resistance to a fifth of the 30 volt coil, the maximum true reading on the dial will only be six volts.

By supplying the meter with a few resistance coils of different values, it is possible for the meter to have many limits.

THE MULTIMETER

If a galvanometer is supplied with a series of shunts and resistances and switches to connect them to the meter, in parallel for the ammeter and in series for the voltmeter, it is possible for one instrument to read not only volts and amperes but volts and amperes in a wide range. Such a device is called a "mutimeter."

USING ELECTRIC METERS

Much of the testing of electric and electronic watches and clocks is observing the condition of the timepiece's various coils and sections of wire.

These coils, which make up the electromagnetic system, are designed either to resist or limit a flow of current or to create electromagnetism. But regardless of its primary purpose, the coil always acts as a resistor.

A longer, thinner wire resists the passage of current more than does a shorter, thicker wire (See Figure 30). Thus, a longer section of wire will create a greater resistance, whether it be a mile long or wound up in a neat coil less than a cubic inch in size.

If a bare length of wire were wound tightly, it would act more like a solid piece of metal than a coil, since there would be no protective insulation to prevent the electrons from taking a shortcut through the coil. This is termed a *short-circuit*. When this occurs, there is little resistance to the current.

Most wire coils are made of copper dipped in an insulating material such as shellac, varnish or plastic, which provides thin but effective insulation and allows the coils to be closely wound. The result is tighter formation of the electromagnetic lines of force.

If some of the insulation is accidentally scraped off or the coil broken by abrasion or heat, a short-circuit results and the electromagnetic qualities of the coil are severely impaired. In an electric clock this results in a weak magnetic impulse and rapid deterioration of the batteries. In a watch, the voltage is diminished or disappears, and either causes a poor balance motion or complete stoppage, with possible deterioration of the batteries.

MEASURING RESISTANCE

If we suspect that a coil is faulty, we can test it by comparing it with figures supplied by the manufacturer which indicate what a coil in good condition should register.

Where there are twin coils in a watch or clock, such as the Lip watch or Swiss clocks, you can compare the two coils in the same timepiece.

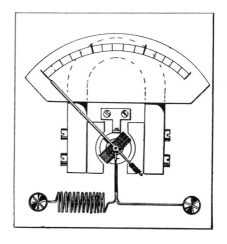

Figure 43

The voltmeter is much like the galvanometer. Because it will be subjected to varying voltages that might burn out the meter, a high resistance coil (lower left) is placed in series with the meter. By supplying this meter with an assortment of calibrated coils, a varied range of voltages may be gauged.

There are many methods of gauging the resistance of a coil. Ohm's law will give us the value in ohms (*electrical symbol-R*), amperes (*electrical symbol-I*) and volts (*electrical symbol-E*). If we know the value of any two of these, we can find the third by using the formulae.

Therefore, if we can measure the voltage drop across the resistance and the amperes, we can discover the resistance in ohms by the formula:

ohms $(R) = \dfrac{\text{volts } (E)}{\text{amperes } (I)}$. If we have an ammeter and a voltmeter, we can obtain the two of these values needed to discover the third, resistance expressed in ohms.

Suppose we suspect the coil of a battery-operated clock to be faulty. We connect our ammeter in series with an electric cell as shown in Figure 44, across the two ends of the coil, and the voltmeter across the winding of the coil. Of course, you must use meters capable of carrying the necessary current. The readings on the ammeter will give you the *intensity* (I), another term for current or amperes; the voltmeter will gauge the *electromotive force* (E), the electrical term for volts. Knowing these two, we can learn the third; *resistance* (R) or ohms.

Assume the voltmeter reads 3 volts and the ammeter indicates a .20 ampere reading. Using the formula:

$$\frac{E}{I} = R; \text{ we see that } \frac{3}{.20} = 15 \text{ ohms.}$$

Most clocks have their correct electrical values stamped on the clock or coil spool. If your figures match those of the maker, the coils are in good condition. Should the ammeter read .5 amperes, the formula:

$$\frac{E}{I} = R \text{ tells us that } \frac{3}{.5} = 6 \text{ ohms.}$$

This would indicate that 3/5 of the coil is inoperative.

Another example: If the maker of this clock had stated that the coil's resistance value is 15 ohms, our formula checks out similarly by

$$\frac{E}{R} = I \text{ or, } \frac{3}{15} = .20 \text{ amps.}$$

THE OHMMETER

While it is possible to obtain resistance values (ohms) by hooking up both a voltmeter and an ammeter, this method is awkward. Today, meters expressly designed to measure resistances alone are available. To understand the working principle of an ohmmeter, assume that you have a galvanometer with a scale reading up to .005 amperes, or 5 milliamperes.

Connect this galvanometer in series with a one-cell battery of 1½ volts and a 450 ohm resistor, as shown in Figure 45, By using Ohm's law again, we find $I = \frac{E}{R}$ or, $\frac{1.5}{450} = .003$ amps, which measures the current flowing through the coil.

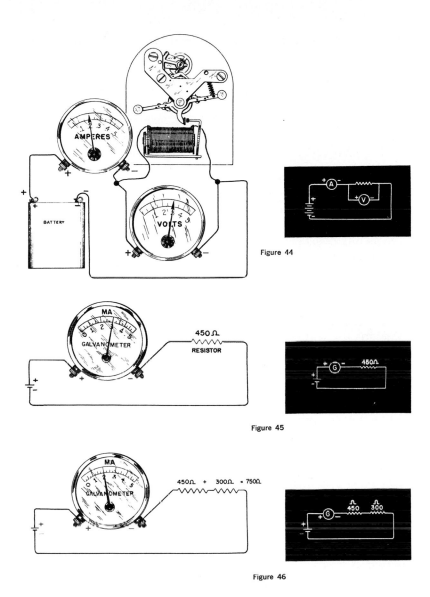

Figure 44

Figure 45

Figure 46

Figure 44 shows the ammeter, voltmeter method of testing the resistance of a clock coil. A galvanometer arranged in series with a battery and known resistor will supply a reading, as shown in Figure 45. An additional resistor is added in Figure 46. The white on black drawings at the right are the same figures expressed solely in electrical symbols.

With the same idea, let us add to the 450 Ω (*The Greek letter omega, Ω, is often used as the symbol of ohms*) resistor another of 300 Ω in series with the first one. The total of resistance in series is the sum of the values of each. Or, in this example, 750 Ω, as shown in Figure 46. Again using Ohm's law, $I = \dfrac{E}{R}$ or, $.002 = \dfrac{1.5}{750}$.

This shows a lower reading on our instrument. By using various resistors, in addition to the 450 Ω resistor in the circuit, it is possible to obtain different readings on our instrument. Even if the instrument had no known scale, we still could calibrate a scale upon it from our known values.

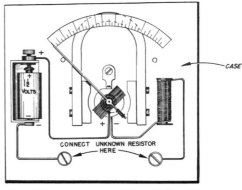

Figure 47

In essence this is the design of an ohmmeter. It is shown in Figure 47. In this illustration we have as our basis the galvanometer hooked up in series with a one cell battery and a resistor of known value. The instrument already knows the value of the reading of the cell it contains (½ volts) and its internal resistor (450 ohms) connecting the two as it produces a scale reading of .003 amperes. Should we connect a resistor of unknown value across the connector points where indicated the scale will read the additional resistance of our newly connected coil. Of course, the instrument could be calibrated to read zero when no additional coil is connected. It would then show only the value of the resistance of the connected coil. Since the strongest current in such a set-up will be indicated if the connections shown are bridged by a short, thick piece of wire, any additional coil in series will show *more* resistance and the instrument's hand will move accordingly to indicate higher resistance and thus weaker current.

Figure 48 shows a multimeter in use. This instrument is a voltmeter, ammeter and ohmmeter combined. It can be used to gauge a number of values in a very wide range. This is possible because it is primarily a galvanometer, that simple device discussed earlier, with some refinements built into it, (Figures 34 to 42).

To use the galvanometer as an ammeter, we placed shunts across its leads. By using many thicknesses of properly stationed shunts, many ampere values can be gauged by providing a suitable switching arrangement to hook the desired shunt to the instrument. To use the galvanometer as a voltmeter, we provided a resistance coil in series with the galvanometer. By using a number of resistance coils of known values and a means of switching the desired resistance to the galvanometer, any range of volts can be safely read on the same galvanometer.

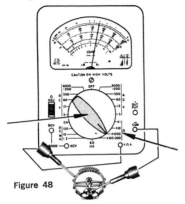

Figure 48

Figure 47 shows the basic principle of an ohmmeter. It has an internal resistance and its own power source, a 1½ volt dry cell. Note that it provides for convenient attachment of an unknown resistor. Study the multimeter shown in Figure 48. Note the many switch adjustments to read amps, volts and ohms of various values.

ometer as a voltmeter, we provided a resistance coil in series with the galvanometer. By using a number of resistance coils of known values and a means of switching the desired resistance to the galvanometer, any range of volts can be safely read on the same galvanometer.

As an ohmmeter, the galvanometer uses its own power source, a dry cell in series with a known resistor adjusted so that its dial reads zero resistance. Switch the unknown resistance in series with the built-in resistor, and the dial reading indicates the value of the unknown resistor. By providing the same galvanometer with a number of different known and calibrated resistances and a switching arrangement to connect any one of them in series with the instrument, a wide range of resistances can be read. It is thus possible to design a galvanometer to read amperes, volts and ohms of various ranges, by providing it with a number of shunts, resistors and a system of switching electrically through the galvanometer's pivoted and moveable coil so that the attached indicator-hand will read the scale.

Let us again examine the multimeter shown in Figure 48. Notice that the contacts are shown touching both ends of the coil of the balance. Such an instrument contains its own energy source, usually a 1½ volt cell switched into the instrument when ohms are gauged. Notice also that the switch is turned so that its pointer is turned to X1000. The "X" in front of the 1000 indicates that any reading on the dial above must be multiplied by 1000.

If the switch were turned to X1, the scale is read directly; that is, multiplied by one. Should the switch be turned to X10 the scale reading is multiplied by 10.

Thus this meter is capable of indicating 100,000 X 200, or 20,000,000 Ω.

In the reading above, in which the leads are connected to the ends of the coil on the Hamilton balance, the switch is multiplying the reading by a thousand. The scale reading points to 3; therefore the reading is 3000, within the tolerance of Hamilton's 500.

When the switch is turned to DVC, the meter can measure volts supplied by direct current from batteries or generators. The coil at the left is for adjusting the instrument, perhaps to read zero should a new battery be used with voltage in excess of 1.50 volts. For example, the energy cells used in the Hamilton 500 electric watch produce 1.57 volts when new. Adjusting to read zero and the volts 1.50 will bring in a required 200 ohm resistance.

ELECTRIC TIMEPIECES — HOW AND WHY THEY WORK

An electric timepiece can use many methods to produce the mechanical impulse needed to move its regulating unit—either a balance, pendulum, tuning fork or others. Most electric watches use a balance and hair spring; while in many small electric clocks, and one early experimental watch, a spring is tensed periodically to move the conventional train of wheels and escapement.

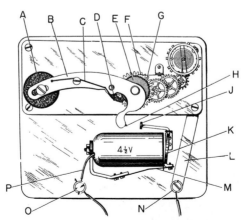

Figure 49—A weighted arm acts like a crank lever to activate the train of wheels and escapement. Arm A is lifted by a "kick" from J when K is magnetically attracted to the coil encased in its metal housing. The circuit is completed when the weighted arm descends and H contacts J. The electric circuit follows leads O and N, through the metal connector L, into the movement. The movement is insulated from the other electrical elements.

Lifted Weight or 'Kick-Type'

In the latter timepieces the impulse or tensing of a helical spring is accomplished by periodically completing an electric circuit. The circuit activates a strong electromagnet which attracts a soft piece of iron. The iron in turn either kicks an arm upon which the spring is mounted, tensing it, or moves a weight upwards, using gravity to power the train of wheels.

Figure 49 shows this arrangement in simplified form. The movement is mounted on a plastic base which insulates it from the electromagnet. The magnet is encased in a metal housing. The coil needs $4\frac{1}{2}$ volts to energize it properly.

The mechanical system is simple—and will help you to understand more complicated units to be explained later.

At A is a weight situated on the extreme left of the arm (B). The lever arm is loosely mounted and pivoted over the center arbor. The center arbor is the same as those used on the standard mainspring type of small clock. Solidly mounted on the center wheel at G is a ratchet wheel (E). Attached to the weighted lever arm (B) is the click (D) and its clickspring (C), which keeps the click engaged with the ratchet (E).

At F is a retaining spring, which is constantly engaged with the ratchet wheel.

If we lift the arm and weight at A with the fingers, the click will slide past the ratchet teeth without moving them, because the ratchet is held in position by the retaining spring (F). As the weight is released it tries to drop. The click, pushing on the ratchet attached to the center wheel, causes the train of wheels to turn, activating the escapement and balance.

This is how it is done electrically:

The weight (A) descends. Its contact piece (H) approaches the kicker arm button (J). H and J make a solid contact, and the circuit is completed.

The $4\frac{1}{2}$-volt battery is connected to the leads O and N. Lead O travels up this junction through P into one end of the coil. The other end of the coil is attached to its metal casing. The casing acts as an extension wire leading from that part of the coil. The casing is connected by the metal arm extending from the rounded rear of the casing into the spring (M) and soft iron disc (K). The disc's extension is bent and terminates at the silver button (J). When J and H are touching, the electric circuit continues through into the movement. The movement, being made of metal, is an electrical conductor.

The circuit continues through the movement and, since electricity generally takes the shortest path to complete a circuit, follows the metal tab or canal (*L*) to the lead (*N*) and the other battery terminal.

When the circuit is completed, the coil within the metal casing becomes energized and attracts the soft iron disc (*K*) with a violent motion.

This causes the button (*J*) to impart an equally sudden kick to *H,* and the arm and weight fly upwards. As the metal disc is drawn to the coil and cannot go further, *H* separates from the button and breaks contact. This broken contact interrupts the circuit, releasing the magnetic attraction. The soft iron disc is forced back to its rest position by the spring (*M*).

In most cases where the contact is the "kick-type" illustrated, the actual contact is a rubbing or wiping motion of the rounded nose (*H*) upon the button (*J*), so that carbon which may accumulate from sparking is wiped away by the action of the contact and impulse.

"Kick-type" clocks are better suited for wall or table where the gravity arm will not be disturbed. This type of clock is advantageous in that the weight, being constant, allows better time-keeping—except for the brief moment when the weight

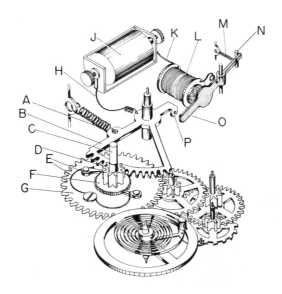

is being lifted. Some of the more expensive clocks have a system of maintaining power while the arm is being lifted so that motion to the train is continuous.

Battery Powered Portables

A system by which electromagnetic impulses are used in portable timepieces is shown in simplified form in Figure 50. Here the motive power is supplied by a helical spring (A) pulling on a sector gear (B). The sector is pivoted, and its teeth enmesh with the center pinion (D), which is separated from the center wheel and mounted loosely on the center post (C). Attached solidly to the center pinion is the ratchet wheel (F). The ratchet's teeth engage the diametrically opposed clicks (E), which are held by a common clickspring against the ratchet teeth. The center wheel (G) is mounted solidly on the center post, and separated from the pinion and ratchet. The clicks and clicksprings (E) are mounted on center wheel (G) and move with it.

While the helical spring (A) is pulling on the sector (B) it is moving clockwise, causing the center pinion (D) to turn counterclockwise. Since the ratchet wheel (F) is part of the pinion, it too moves counterclockwise against the beaks of the clicks (E). Because the clicks are attached to the center wheel, they cannot move unless the center wheel moves. The center pinion and ratchet, through the clicks, causes the center wheel to turn counterclockwise and activate the train of wheels and escapement.

The electrical circuit has been simplified as follows:

The electric cell in its housing (J) has one end, at the lead wire H, grounded to the movement at the rack. The other battery terminal has a lead wire (K) attached directly to one end of the coil (L). The other end of the coil's wire is attached to the pivoted soft iron disc (O). As shown, the circuit is incomplete or "open." As the tensing of the coiled helical spring moves the sector closer, the opposite end of the sector arm (P) contacts the extension of the soft iron piece (O), completing the circuit.

With the circuit completed the coil becomes an electromagnet, designed so that a strong and sudden magnetic pull is exerted at (O), towards the coil's core. This sudden, strong pull causes the extension to thrust the arm (P) counterclockwise. The sector's teeth also turn counterclockwise. Because the pinion is enmeshed with the sector's teeth, it turns in a clockwise direction. The pinion's attached ratchet wheel (*F*) skips past the beaks of the opposed clicks (*E*).

This motion continues until the initial force of the magnetic impulse and momentum equal the tension of the extended helical spring (*A*). The spring again takes over, causes the sector to move clockwise, and the train revolves.

While this system is more versatile than the lifted-weight system, the spring causes a variation in balance motion. When the spring is fully tensed at the beginning of the impulse it is strong and the balance motion is great. When the spring is almost run down and contact is near, balance motion falls off. Many clocks using this system employ a long spring, and design it so only its middle portion is used. But even then the motion variation is present if the impulse is not delivered frequently. Frequent impulse, on the other hand, reduces a battery's life expectancy.

A system such as the one illustrated in Figure 50 was miniaturized by Dr. A. L. Rawlings in his experiments to make an electric wrist watch in 1954. The movement used was a 5½ ligne. It worked well, although the watch had to be housed in a 12-ligne case.

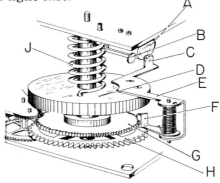

Figure 51. In this system the electromagnetic impulse is similar to that shown in Figure 49 and 50, except that the helical spring is subjected to torque winding instead of being powered by gravity or a flexed spring. Flywheel D helps to wind helical spring J. The flywheel is separated from the wheels below, and attached to the hollow tube around which the helical spring is twisted. The ratchet and center wheels move as one unit.

Another type of electric timepiece in which a helical spring supplies the motive power to turn the train of wheels is illustrated in Figure 51. Instead of the spring being pulled in the usual manner, however, it is subjected to torque tension and wound similarly to a conventional mainspring. To simplify this example the number of turns in the helical spring has been reduced.

A is the coil casing and *B* the soft iron piece. *B* is attracted to the far end of the coil when the coil is energized by the completed circuit.

The button on the soft iron piece (*B*) kicks the tab (*C*). The tab is positioned upon a heavy disc (*D*) which serves as a flywheel. *E* is an extension of the metal piece. It is fastened to the flywheel (*D*) and acts as a bridge for the pivoted click (*F*). The clickspring is a very weak helical spring. The click (*F*) engages the ratchet (*G*), which is solidly mounted on the center wheel (*H*). The helical spring (*J*), which supplies the power, has one end fastened to the upper plate; its other end terminates at the flywheel.

The flywheel (*D*) is mounted on a hollow tube which is loosely fitted on the center post. The ratchet and center wheels are one unit riveted to the center post. Thus the flywheel can turn independently of the rachet and center wheels.

When the electric circuit is completed as *B* contacts *C*, *B* thrusts *C* clockwise. Since *C* is mounted on the flywheel (*D*), the flywheel also moves clockwise, winding the helical spring (*J*) around its hollow tube. While the flywheel is being thrust clockwise, the click (*F*) trips past the teeth of the ratchet wheel (*G*). The helical spring takes over, pulls the flywheel counterclockwise and the click (*F*), butting against the ratchet teeth, moves the attached center wheel with it, activating the train of wheels. In this sequence the flywheel is moving as one unit with the center wheels and ratchet. Tab (*C*) again approaches *B* until contact is made, and the cycle repeated.

Third-Wheel System

In some clocks employing this principle the helical spring is mounted on the third wheel instead of the center wheel. When this is done a weaker and longer spring can be used to achieve better timekeeping, due to a minimum variation in balance motion. Mounting this arrangement on the third wheel permits the use of an electromagnet requiring only one dry cell. While this method requires more frequent impulses, it does not drain the electric cell or battery; and noise made during the sudden and strong mechanical impulse is kept to a minimum. Of course such a system is used only where the thickness of the movement is of no importance.

When this third-wheel system is used, the helical spring and click-ratchet reverse their direction.

Some clocks which use this system have an auxiliary spring

that maintains power to the train of wheels while the electrical impulse is imparted to the mainspring in the opposite direction. The use of a coiled spring wound electrically has some advantages over an axially flexed or pulled helix. Aside from conserving height, the power it imparts is generally more uniform and lends itself better to isochronal timing.

Battery-powered timepieces using springs of all types frequently have the springs mounted in conjunction with the third wheel, instead of the center wheel as pictured here for simplicity. With the springs on the third wheel a single electric cell may be used. Other advantages are easier winding, a smaller electric cell and certain improvements. While the contacts are more frequent, they are weaker.

If an electrical system were designed to wind a spring to run a timepiece for a longer time, the number of cells would have to be increased to supply the additonal power. Since the life of each cell presumably would be the same as the cell in a clock using one cell, the cost of batteries would be greater—without providing advantages to offset the cost. In addition, the impulse and coil winding would have to be very powerful to overcome the natural resistance of a spring strong enough to motivate a train of wheels for a long period.

In our next chapter we will show how one manufacturer overcomes these obstacles while using only one energy cell.

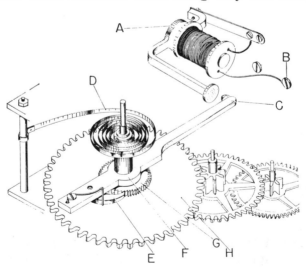

Figure 52. The movement shown here is thinner than the ones illustrated previously. A weak mainspring drives the train of wheels and escapement.

Thinner Movement

A system with a thinner movement is shown in Figure 52. A weak mainspring is used to drive the train of wheels and traditional escapement. Carefully observe the illustration and you will be able to understand this system easily.

A is a soft iron push-piece. It is attached to a thin, flat return spring. *A* serves as an electrical connection to one end of the coil. The coil and all of its attachments are insulated from the movement and battery mounting. *B* is a connection to one terminal of the coil and the battery. The movement itself serves as both the "ground" and a connection to the other lead of the battery.

When the contact button on the arm (*C*) touches *A*'s button, the circuit is completed. The energized coil quickly and energetically draws the soft iron piece (*A*) to it. This causes the arm (*C*) to be "kicked" clockwise, pivoting at *F*. The click (*E*) ratchets past the teeth of the ratchet (*G*) and winds the mainspring (*D*) until the momentum of the electromagnetic kick is overcome. The mainspring takes over by moving the hollow arbor counterclockwise. The arm (*F*) is riveted or otherwise fastened to the mainspring arbor, which is hollow and rides easily on the center post.

The impulse arm (*F*) is attached to the lower post of the hollow arbor; and the click and spring (*E*) are attached to it. The rachet wheel (*G*) and the center wheel (*H*) are attached to each other and move as one unit.

When the rachet is pushed counterclockwise by the beak of the click (*E*), the train is also moved counterclockwise until the arm (*C*) again makes contact with the coil's soft iron piece (*A*).

A MOTOR-WOUND ELECTRIC CLOCK

This German clock uses a toy-sized direct current motor, energized by a single small battery, to power its escapement.

We said that one manufacturer had overcome the obstacles inherent in powering a clock with only one cell. The manufacturer, Diehl, of Schramberg, Germany, uses a "toy-sized" direct current motor. The motor shaft is geared low enough to wind the spring so that power can be stored and applied for a long period of time. The Diehl movement is pictured in Figure 53.

FIGURE 53

The motor which powers the movement uses only 105 milliamperes per second on 1½ volts, yet winds the helical spring enough to allow a full turn of the third wheel, to provide a running time of eight minutes. The motor requires 1½ to 2 seconds to wind the helical spring, allowing the battery to recover for eight minutes before the next drain on the cell.

Should the battery's voltage drop below 1.5 volts, it would take a bit longer for the motor to wind the helical mainspring, perhaps two seconds instead of the 1½ needed with a fresh battery. The use of a helical mainspring, that is, using a wire with a round cross-section, virtually eliminates the need for lubrication and is said to be practically breakproof.

Infrequent use of the battery's power for winding and the short period during which the battery is used guarantees it a long life. The motor is meshed with the clock by a worm gear, which requires one full motor turn for each tooth. There are 48 teeth, so the motor must revolve 48 times to wind the helical wire in a complete winding sequence. The torque is lower than that ordinarily required by a motor geared to a pinion and wheel, where the ratio is larger. The worm gear also provides quieter winding.

How It Works

Figure 54 shows the principles of this system. The motor's rotor (*A*) has the worm drive (*F*) on its shaft, which is enmeshed with a nylon worm wheel (*R*). This plastic wheel is mounted loosely on the third wheel arbor. A helical wire mainspring (*U*) is fastened to the bottim of the third wheel at one end (*L*), and

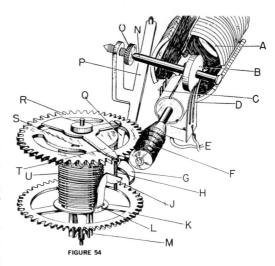

FIGURE 54

connected at the top of the nylon worm wheel (*R*) at *S*.

The motor turns clockwise, and the worm (*F*) turns the worm wheel (*R*) clockwise. The helical spring (*U*) is tensed and supplies power, through the third wheel (*K*), to the train of wheels. The pinion (*M*) is enmeshed with the center wheel and dial train.

A switching sequence turns the motor on and off either at each eight-minute interval or as soon as the mainspring is wound. If the motor were to continue to wind the mainspring tight on its cylinder, rebounding of the balance as well as undue drain on the battery would result.

Electrical Contact

The electrical connection to the motor is made as the brushes (*C and D*) contact the segmented commutator. The brushes are made of a spring metal which is a good electrical conductor. Brush *D* is taller than brush *C*. Brush *C* is on the left in our illustration. Mounted horizontally above the brushes is a metal rod (*N*), which rests in bushings (*not pictured*). Near the right end of the rod is a plastic disc (*B*). The edge of the disc intersects the tips of brush *D*. The disc is frictioned to the rod (*N*). The springy brushes are nearly always on the plastic disc (*B*), applying pressure to the left in an attempt to force contact with the commutator.

However, in the sequence shown in Figure 54 the locked position of the rod (*N*) is keeping brush *D* from making contact with the commutator—thus the motor is not working.

43

The pressure on the rod's rounded end by the flat screw-head (O), which is threaded into the elbow of the pivoted locking lever (P), keeps the rod (N) and disc (B) locked and the motor at rest. The pivoted locking lever (P) is kept in position so that its elbow's screw (O) presses to the right to keep the brushes from electrical contact with the motor's commutator. The pin (H) reaches downward through the concentric slot in the wheel (R). It remains in this position until the vertical extension (J), attached solidly to the third wheel (K) and moving with it, makes one full revolution. As it comes around, almost completing a full circuit, its flat extension (J) makes contact with the pin (H). Although the pin is mounted firmly to the three-armed floating piece (T), the floating piece is mounted loosely on the third wheel arbor and is free to turn. The face of the extension (J) makes contact with the pin (H). The pin continues to move until it leaves the corner of the lock lever at G and enters the curved, concentric surface at G. J continues to move H until H is past the beak of G.

At this point the pressure of the spring-brush (D) on the disc (B) moves the disc, its rod (N) and the lever (P) to the left. An electrical contact is made and the motor turned on.

The motor turns at about 1900 revolutions per minute, or about 48 turns in 1½ seconds, using a 1½-volt cell. The worm (F) turns clockwise which moves the worm wheel (R) clockwise.

When contact is first made as the pin falls past the beak G, the pin (H) has been pushed in a circular path in the concentric slot (Q) by the extension piece (J). At this point of electrical contact, the pin (H) is near the forward end of the slot (Q). When the worm wheel (R) is being turned by the worm (F), the pin is motionless until the back end of the circular slot catches up with it and carries it along, together with the three-armed free piece (T).

Movement continues until the pointed extension at T enmeshes with the worm and is carried along with the worm wheel (R). The pin makes contact with the flat end of the lock lever (P) and forces it to the right. This movement in turn causes the button-head screw (O) to push the horizontal rod (N) to the right, and the plastic disc (B) pushes back the spring-brush (D). The electrical contact is broken and the motor stops.

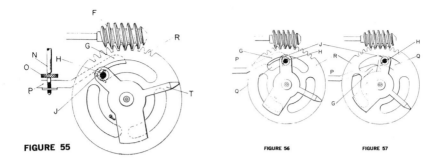

FIGURE 55

FIGURE 56

FIGURE 57

Figure 55: The concentric slot (Q) provides latitude of movement for the pin (H). T allows the pin an extra margin of movement during winding.

Figure 56: The pin has moved almost half the length of its slot, and is shown near the end of the beak (G).

Figure 57: Now the pin has passed the beak (G). Under pressure from the commutator spring-brush, the entire piece (P and G) falls downward.

A Closer Look

In Figure 55 the position of the extension (*J*) is practically where it was when it caused the pin (*H*) to trip off the beak of *G*.

The concentric slot (*Q*) provides additional latitude of movement for the pin (*H*). The pointed toothshaped piece at *T* provides an extra margin of movement for the pin during winding, when *J* makes one complete revolution and moves it.

Figures 55, 56 and 57 show the sequence in two dimensions.

Each part bears the same identifying letter in all of the drawings. In Figure 55 the pin (*H*) has come to a stop after being forced around by the worm wheel (*R*) and the end of the slot. The pin (*H*) has forced the lever (*G*) upward. The lever (*G*) exerts pressure at *P* to move the screw (*O*), which moves the rod (*N*) and pushes the springbrush away from the commutator of the motor. This breaks the circuit, and the motor stops.

The third wheel has run for about seven minutes. Its extension piece (*J*) has almost completed a full revolution and is against the pin (*H*).

In Figure 56 the flat extension piece (*J*) is moving the pin freely in its slot so that the pin rides along on the curved surface of the locking lever's beak (*G*). It is shown here almost at the end of the beak. Note that the pin (*H*) has moved almost half the length of its slot (*Q*).

In Figure 57 the pin has moved a bit more, past the beak (*G*) which, through the pressure of the commutator spring-

45

brush has caused the piece (*P* and *G*) to fall downward. An electrical contact is made as the brush touches the commutator. The motor turns. The worm moves the worm wheel (*R*) clockwise until the rear of the slot (*Q*) in which the pin rides comes against the pin (*H*), and moves it until it is again positioned as shown in Figure 55.

The extension of the third wheel (*J*) is in about the same position as shown in Figure 57, since it moves only with the third wheel. The pin (*H*) appears as in Figure 55, except that it is behind the extension piece (*J*).

No restraint is required as the worm gathers up the wheel since the gear ratio of wheel to worm is too high to move it backwards, regardless of the strength of the mainspring. This is an advantage because it reduces friction during winding.

A SIMPLE ELECTRIC MOTOR — how it works

Because repair of motor-wound timepieces requires attention to their motors, knowledge of a direct current motor's principles of operation is important to the watchmaker.

Direct current motors and the balances of electric watches have much in common. Both contain electromagnets pivoting on axes, which are attracted or repelled by permanent magnets when polarized by a battery's current.

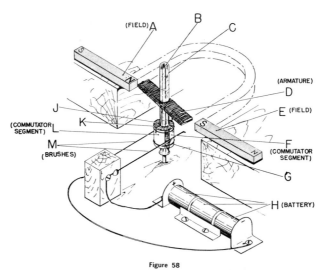

Figure 58

This simple device, easily fabricated from materials available in the home or shop, demonstrates the basic principles of operation of the motors used to power an electric timepiece.

Unlike balances, which oscillate back and forth, motors turn continuously in one direction. You can make a simple experimental motor, shown in Figure 58, to help you understand more about them and how they work.

Obtain a glass tube or a thin test tube (C), a flat piece of soft iron about 2 inches long and ½-in. wide, and a bottle cork about an inch in diameter (J).

Drill a hole through the center of the cork, and force the test tube into it to about ½" above the tube's mouth. Drill a hole through the iron's flat center, and shellac the tube in place about an inch above the cork. Remove the insulation from one piece of insulated copper wire and position it against the cork's side. Bring the wire up the outside of the tube, along the underside of the bar to its outer end, and wind a neat clockwise coil of wire around the bar, past the test tube to the other side. Turn the end of the wire back so that it doesn't unravel. Bring it back to the test tube, and position it so that it remains against the cork. Scrape the insulation from both ends of the wire.

Cut two squares of copper or tin foil (L and F) and position them around the cork so that the distance between them is equal, and there is about ¼-inch clearance on each side. Place rubber bands over the exposed ends so that the ends are pressed firmly on the square plates. Make sure that each plate is facing one side of the coiled wire on the bar (D).

Use a large board as a base. Drive a long thin nail upward through the bottom of the board so that the hollow tube rests and pivots on it. Cut a small block of wood, about the thickness of the cork and high enough to be level with the top of the cork (J).

Scrape the insulation from the ends of two pieces of springy copper wire. Twist the wire to give it more "springiness." Secure the wires to the small block of wood so that they are parallel to each other on opposite sides of the wood block at the same height and length. Use two screws for each wire; position them as shown. The wires should be long enough to make contact with the plates. The loose ends of the wires (M) can be connected to a large dry cell or a group of cells (H). A convenient way to make contact with the batteries is to use scraps of sheet metal. Do not connect the wires to the battery yet.

The core of the motor is finished. To complete the motor,

we need either two bar magnets (*A* and *E*) resting on blocks of wood to provide height, or a horseshoe magnet (shown by the dotted lines) placed on a block of wood of the correct height. The horseshoe magnet must be wide enough to embrace the coil without its ends touching. In the absence of either bar or horseshoe magnets, magnetize a couple of files in your watch de-magnetizer and position them on the wood blocks close to the coil (*D*), being careful not to interfere with the rotation of the pivoting, coil-wound bar. Before connecting the battery to the loose ends of the wires (*M*), spin the bar (*D*) by hand and assure that it clears both magnets, and yet passes close to them. Assure that the wires leading from the coil are in solid contact with the plates. Check to see that the wires are free of insulating lacquer and oxides. Finally, make certain that the wires (*M*) begin to make contact with the plates *after* the coil-bar (*D*) has *passed* the point where it is on-line with the long axis of the bar magnets. Adjust the plates to make sure the sequence is correct.

If you have followed directions accurately, the wires (*M*) will be resting on the cork between the plates (*L* and *F*) when the bar (*D*) is on line with the magnets. Of course the magnets should be positioned with opposite poles facing each other.

Connect the battery leads and your motor should start turning clockwise. If it doesn't move, give it a nudge in either direction. If it turns, but again positions itself opposite the magnets, there is probably an open circuit. Check the wires' contact with the plates. If there is current flowing through the wires and into the coil, there will be an electromagnetic surge—but the leads may be crossed. Change the leads so that the wires end at opposite terminals of the battery. The "motor" should now turn.

Current and Polarity

The current flows from the battery through the positive terminal. It travels through the wires (*M*), or *brushes,* to the plates, which are called commutators. The wires (*K*), making contact with the commutators from above, bring the current into the coil wound around the iron bar, which becomes an electromagnet. This part of a motor is called the *armature.* The electromagnetic polarity is such that the north pole of the armature is adjacent to the north pole of the permanent magnet. Since like poles repel, the north poles move away from each other and cause the armature to spin clockwise. At the same time, the brush on the right makes contact with the other commutator (*F*), causing the coil to become polarized with its south pole adjacent to the south pole of the permanent magnet (*E*). This too causes the pivoting armature to be pushed clockwise.

When the armature has made a 180° turn, the brush at the right makes contact with the other commutator segment, with its attached wire (*K*). The polarity is reversed and the clockwise motion maintained.

If the armature were turned counter-clockwise by hand from the position shown in Figure 58, the brushes (*M*) would touch the cork sections between the commutator segments when the armature is on line with the magnets. Move the armature a bit further and right brush makes contact with the edge of the commutator (*L*) and causes this section of the armature to act as a north pole, because its wire lead from the commutator starts at the left wing of the armature. This results in an attraction of the armature, and it returns in a clockwise direction. As it does, the armature again approaches a position opposite the magnets. The brushes contact the insulating cork. The momentum carries the armature past the center line of the bar magnets, and the brushes again make contact.

Repulsion of like poles again results, and the motor continues to turn clockwise.

Thus, such a motor turns in one direction only. The direction depends on the winding of the coil and the connections to the battery. If the battery were reversed, the motor would turn in the opposite direction.

Electrical Terms

In learning the names of the motor parts—whether the motor is the balance of an electric watch or one supplying power to wind a clock—the names indicated in Figure 58 are generally used. The magnets, which are part of the stationary housing of the motor, are called the *field*. Sometimes the field is called the *stator* (meaning *stationary*). The turning electromagnets, and in some cases a pivoting permanent magnet, are called the *armature* or *rotor*. However, it is more apt to be called a *rotor* when the turning part contains permanent magnets, as in the Secticon, made by Universal Escapements Ltd., and in synchronous electric clocks.

Where the armature is an electromagnet, current must be supplied to energize the moving coil. One end of the coil's wire is soldered to a segment which "commutes" current from an electrical source to the armature. This segment must be made wide enough to carry current through most of the armature's turn. This part is called the *commutator,* shown in Figure 58 as *L* and *F*. As an electric train receives current from a third rail through "shoes," the wires (*M*) conduct current to the commutator.

In a watch like the Hamilton 500, the contact wires become the brushes and the gold pin becomes the commutator. The balance is the armature and the permanent magnets under the balance together with the shunt pieces comprise the field.

In the Swiss electric watch, too, the contact wires serve as brushes. The contact tab is termed the commutator and the balance, containing a permeable alloy rather than a coil, is called the rotor.

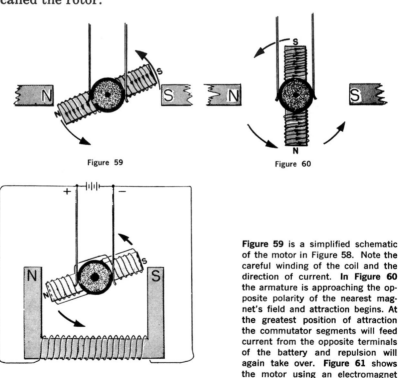

Figure 59

Figure 60

Figure 61

Figure 59 is a simplified schematic of the motor in Figure 58. Note the careful winding of the coil and the direction of current. In Figure 60 the armature is approaching the opposite polarity of the nearest magnet's field and attraction begins. At the greatest position of attraction the commutator segments will feed current from the opposite terminals of the battery and repulsion will again take over. Figure 61 shows the motor using an electromagnet instead of permanent magnets.

The coil on the armature is wound a bit more carefully and shows the clockwise direction of winding and the direction of the current. In Figure 59 the armature is being repelled by the similarity of adjacent poles. As it reaches the position shown in Figure 60, the armature is approaching.

the opposite polarity of the nearest magnet's field and attraction, rather than repulsion, begins. As soon as they are at the greatest position of attraction, the commutator segments feed current from the opposite terminals of the battery, and as it passes beyond this point, repulsion again takes over.

The field can be an electromagnet as well as a permanent magnet. This is shown in Figure 61. Soft iron is used here as a permeable metal core for the electromagnet. An electromagnetic field can be adjusted to the quality desired, although permanent magnets are used in practically all clock motors.

Obstacles

While the simple motors shown in Figures 58-61 work and are easily understood, they have obvious drawbacks. If current was cut off and the motor came to a stop so that the brushes touched the sections between the commutator segments and rested upon the insulating core, the motor couldn't start by itself. Or, as shown in Figure 60, the armature's magnetic influence may be too far from the field's attraction to overcome inertia and friction and get the motor started.

Next, will be described how battery-powered clock motors overcome these obstacles.

We learned the prinicples of operation of a simple electric motor. But we concluded with the disconcerting thought that once the motor stopped it might not start again without help.

Now we examine an inexpensive direct current motor that will start automatically from any position. The motor is shown in Figure 62.

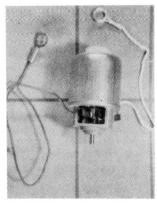

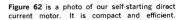
Figure 62 is a photo of our self-starting direct current motor. It is compact and efficient.

FIGURE 62

Three sections to the armature and two permanent magnets in the field are necessary components.

The Field Magnets

The North pole of one curved magnet faces the South pole of the opposite magnet. As we have already learned, it is possible to orient the poles of a magnet to any position.

In order to conserve space, as well as obtain a better motor

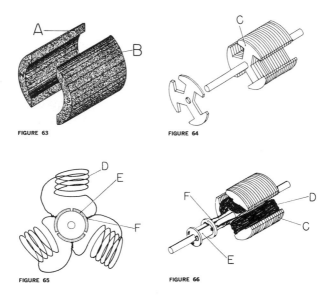

FIGURE 63

FIGURE 64

FIGURE 65

FIGURE 66

action, the field magnets appear as in Figure 63, with the North pole of one curved surface facing the South pole, which is the inner curved surface of the other magnetic field.

Since the field magnets are designed with their curved surfaces of opposite polarity, the electromagnets situated on the rotor or armature must exert a magnetic push, or pull, in conformity with the field magnets. The electromagnetic coil is wound in a flat loop, long enough to allow its magnetic lines of force to interact with those of the field magnets.

Laminated Armature Core

An electromagnet functions more efficiently if its coil is wound on a soft iron core. Efficiency is increased even more if the core is made of laminations or thin layers of iron. The armature core—around which our armature coil will be wound —is made of three-finned plates (*C*), packed together and aligned upon an axle as shown in Figure 64.

Direction Determines Polarity

The coils are wrapped around each section with a continuous length of copper wire, each connected to the next in series (*Figure 65*). *D* is the coil. It is soldered to the commutator segment (*E*). With the coil wound as shown, a positive current fed to the upper part of the coil causes it to become an electromagnet, with the North pole at the top and South pole at the the bottom.

The lower part of each coil is connected to the commutator segment at *F*. Note that the coil is wound upwards and around, to assure the proper polarity when current flows through it.

Figure 66 shows how the three coils appear when wound around the armature core. The beginning of one coil and end of the next coil are joined together at *F*. Point *D*, Figure 65, shows that the coils are wound in the same direction. To insulate the commutator segments from each other, a plastic sleeve is placed over the forward part of the armature axle. On the axle is the commutator with its three separated metal segments, each insulated from the other (*E, Figure 66*). They are made of silver, which is a good electrical conductor. The commutator segments transfer electrical energy from the battery to the coils.

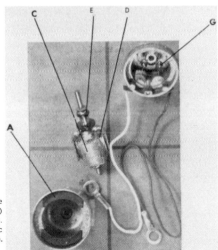

This is our motor broken down into its three main sections. Note that the field magnet (A) is positioned by lead shims in an iron casing. This construction concentrates the magnetic lines of force and protects steel parts from them.

FIGURE 67

PARTS IDENTIFIED

Figure 67 is a photograph of the motor with its three chief sections dismantled. *A* is a field magnet, positioned by lead shims inside an iron casing. The construction concentrates the field magnet's lines of force and protects nearby steel parts from their influence. *C* is the armature. *D* is the wire coil wound around one of the sections. *E* is one of the three silver commutator segments and *G* one of the brushes which will rub against them.

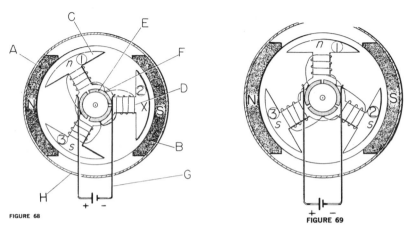

FIGURE 68

FIGURE 69

Figure 68 shows the first phase. Note that one coil is inactive. In Figure 69 a fraction of a second has elapsed and the armature has turned 30° or 1/12-turn to the right. For the only time during the motor's four phases of operation all three armature sections are energized.

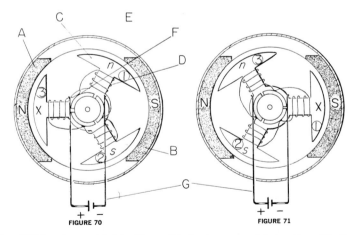

FIGURE 70

FIGURE 71

Another 30° has been added in Figure 70. Again, one coil is inactive, this time the one on armature section three. After another partial turn the motor appears as in Figure 71, and armature section one is "dead."

The motor sequence is shown in four phases in Figures 68-71. *A* is the North pole magnet, situated between lead shims contained in the iron shell casing (*H*). *B* is the South pole magnet. *C* is one of the three armature sections. For simplicity we show an abbreviated winding of the armature coils

54

around each armature section (D). E is one of the three silver commutator segments. At F the end of each coil makes contact with the commutator and the beginning of the next coil. G is one of the two brushes; the one leading to the negative side of the energy cell.

MOTOR SEQUENCE — PHASE ONE

In Figure 68 the positive brush contacts a commutator segment. Positive current flows into the coils, one of which is wound around armature section one and the other around armature section three. However the current enters the two coils from different directions. When the positive current enters the coil on section one, it causes an electromagnetic field with its North pole at the top, as indicated by n. This same current, entering the coil on section three from the bottom, causes the North pole of this section to be at the bottom and the South pole to be at the curved, outer part of the armature section (s).

A COIL "SHORTS OUT"

What is happening to armature section two? If we examine the brush feeding negative current to the commutator, we find that the brush is contacting two commutator segments. Follow the upper right commutator segment to the lead at F, and we discover that one coil connected at that point leads to the end of the coil of armature section one, thus completing the circuit in that coil and causing armature section one to become an electromagnet with the North pole at the top. Follow the brush at the right as it contacts the commutator segment at the lower right, and we find that a coil connected to it goes to armature section three, thus completing the circuit and placing the South pole at the outer, top section of the armature.

Again, follow the contacts made by the negative brush (G) and the two leads from the contacts to the coil on armature section two. By following the lead at F as the wire goes to the top of the coil on section two, we can see that this would ordinarily cause a South pole at the top of this armature section. However, the same brush contacts the commutator segment at the lower right. Following the wire leading to the coil on section two, we find that the same negative current is being drawn into the bottom of the coil. With negative current being fed through both ends of the same coil, the coil "shorts out" and becomes temporarily inactive.

FOUR MAGNETS

We now have four magnets in this little motor. *A* and *B* are permanent *positive* and *negative* field magnets. Armature section one acts as a North pole and section three as a South pole. We know that like magnetic poles repel and unlike magnetic poles attract each other. In the first phase (*Figure 68*), section one is repelled by permanent field magnet *A* while at the same time it attracts South pole armature section three. Section two, marked *x*, has been shorted out and is idle.

In phase two of our motor's sequence of operation (*Figure 69*), the armature has moved clockwise 30° or 1/12 turn, and each brush contacts only one commutator segment. The positive brush at the left still makes contact with the same commutator segment as in the first phase of operation (*Figure 68*). Thus the polarities of armature sections one and three are the same as in Figure 68.

The negative brush now contacts only the upper right commutator segments. This sends negative current through the wire leading to the coil on armature section two. To complete the circuit on this armature section, the positive brush contacts the commutator segment at the left and sends positive current through the bottom of the coil on section three.

The current continues to the top of the coil, onto the lower commutator segment and then to the wire leading to the bottom of the coil on armature section two. The inner, lower part of armature section two becomes a North pole and the outer, top portion a South pole.

FIVE MAGNETS

Now we have three electromagnets and two permanent magnets. Armature section one is mid-way between the North and South field magnets while armature section three is below the center of the North field magnet and section two is past the center of the South field magnet. The result is a clockwise motion.

The North field magnet, attracts armature section three, which has become a South pole, strengthening the clockwise motion. Armature section two, also a South pole, is repelled by the South field magnet, adding more impetus to the clockwise motor action. Armature section one is, of course, repelled by the North field magnet and attracted by the South field magnet.

PHASE THREE — MOTOR SEQUENCE

Now, let us consider the third phase (*Figure 70*). Another 30° has been added to the clockwise motion of the motor. Armature section one is within the influence of the South field magnet (*B*), armature section three is directly opposite the North field magnet (*A*) and armature section two is leaving the area of the South field magnet.

The positive brush touches two commutator segments. Positive current is fed into both ends of the coil around armature section three, and it "shorts out" and becomes temporarily inactive.

The positive brush contacts the upper left commutator segment, sending positive current through *F* to the top of the coil around section one (*D*). To complete the circuit on this section of the armature, the negative brush touches the commutator segment at the right, which supplies a path for the current to complete its circuit.

TRACING THE CURRENT

Once again, let's trace the flow of current into armature section one. It starts at the positive lead of the energy cell, flows through the left brush into the upper left commutator segment, through the coil, down into the upper right commutator segment and out through the brush leading to the negative side of the energy cell. The result—a North pole at the outer part of this armature section (*n*).

Armature section two is a South pole. Follow the flow of current from the positive lead of the battery through the left brush, which also makes contact with the lower left commutator segment. The lower left segment supplies current to the inner end of the coil on armature section two. This positive current continues to flow out of the outer end of the coil to the right commutator segment, and then into the right brush (*G*) and the negative terminal of the battery.

This circuitry causes a North pole at the inner portion of armature section two and a South pole at the outer end of the armature section (*s*).

FOUR MAGNETS AGAIN

Thus, in the third phase we have four magnets, two being field magnets and two being armature-electromagnets. Armature section one is attracted to the South field magnet while armature section two is repelled by it. Clockwise motion is thus maintained. There is neither "pull" nor "push" on the third armature section because it has "shorted out" and remains idle (x).

Of course, after a partial turn the positive brush will touch only the lower left commutator segment, and positive current will flow through the top of the coil on section three, causing a North pole on its outer surface. The circuit will be completed as the current flows through the negative brush, and the North field magnet will repel the North pole of this armature section.

PHASE FOUR — MOTOR SEQUENCE

For the final phase of this motor action, examine Figure 71. Armature section one is in exactly the same position occupied by armature section two in the first phase of motor action (*Figure 68*).

Armature section one and its coil are inactive because the negative brush contacts two commutator segments which supply current to it. Again, a double dose of negative current "shorts out" the armature section (x). Armature section three has a positive polarity at its outer end because the brush at the left transfers positive current along the upper part of the armature section. The circuit is completed as the current travels outward into the commutator segment at the upper right, through the negative brush which contacts the commutator segment, and down into one negative terminal of the energy cell.

Armature section two has a negative polarity because positive current enters from the bottom of the coil, goes through the top of the coil and into the lower right commutator segment, and then into the right brush, terminating in the negative part of the battery.

Thus, the field magnet repels section three and attracts section two. A split second later the motor turns slightly. Armature section one becomes a South pole at its outer end, because the right brush only contacts one commutator segment and the circuit to section one is completed through the coil of section two. The South pole in section one is repelled by the South field magnet.

The stronger the energy cell or voltage of the battery, the stronger the electromagnetism and hence the more powerful the motor action. The more powerful the motor action, the faster the motor will go.

At this point the entire four-phase sequence begins again. If the motor were stopped during any of the four phases of operation it would start again automatically, since two of the three coils are energized whenever current is applied to the motor.

CHANGING MOTOR DIRECTION

Should we reverse the battery and make the right brush positive and the left brush negative, the direction of the motor, too, would change. In direct current motors a change in direction is accomplished by switches which reverse the battery leads connected to the brushes.

There are some variations of this motor principle, and some larger motors work on different winding—but the basic principle is much the same. The brushes in some small motors are made of a group of short, fine copper wires bunched together to resemble a small brush. This is said to provide better commutator contact.

Some motors have no permanent magnets in the field. Instead they have separate windings which supply electromagnetism of the desired polarity and power; thus both the field and armature rely on electromagnets. Larger motors use electromagnets exclusively because it is difficult to make large permanent magnets of the desired strength and polarity.

SPARKING: ITS CAUSES AND CURES

A current of electricity, like a flow of water, has momentum. When it is shut off suddenly, a spark may "leak" across contact points causing wear and inefficiency.

Electric timepieces use switches or contacts to turn on a current. Often, these contacts are of very simple design and construction. A circuit is completed, say, when one metallic tab on the balance staff or pendulum makes passing contact with another tab anchored to the movement. This releases energy from a cell or battery which energizes an electromagnetic coil. This in turn attracts or repels the balance, pendulum or tuning fork.

The efficiency of the timepiece and the length of its carefree maintenance period to a large degree depend on these switches and their condition.

Most often, these contact switches are made of gold, silver or platinum to resist wear due to friction and sparking.

Sparking occurs at switchpoints when a contact or circuit is broken, and is less pronounced in watches with a hollow coil, then in those which have a solid or permeable core. Carbon deposits form on the contacts because of the spark. These deposits insulate the tips, prevent good electrical contact and cause poor motion. Eventually the timepiece stops. Furthermore, sparking burns away metal at contact points until the contacts cannot meet, and the watch mechanism stops running permanently.

EXPERIMENT PROVES IT

A simple experiment will prove that sparking is caused by the coil, and that it takes place when the circuit is broken rather than when it is closed.

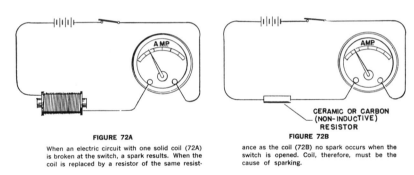

FIGURE 72A

FIGURE 72B

When an electric circuit with one solid coil (72A) is broken at the switch, a spark results. When the coil is replaced by a resistor of the same resist-

ance as the coil (72B) no spark occurs when the switch is opened. Coil, therefore, must be the cause of sparking.

Hook an ammeter into a circuit which includes an energy source and a coil of many turns, as schematized in Figure 72A. Start a current through the circuit and notice that while the switch is closed there is no sparking. Also, read the value of the ammeter.

Now, break the circuit by opening the switch. A strong spark should occur there. Repeat this, replacing the coil with a carbon or ceramic resistor of the same resistance as the coil (*Figure 72B*). This time there should be little or no sparking, but the current reading on the ammeter will be the same.

Since the coil is the only thing that has been changed, it must have been the cause of the strong sparking in Figure 72A. Specifically, it is the destruction of a magnetic field in the coil which causes the spark.

SIMILAR TO PLUMBING

It is possible to understand the causes and cures of sparking by a simple analogy from hydraulics.

When we open a faucet, a flow of water begins and continues to flow until it is shut off or the supply is exhausted. In an electrical circuit the same is true: electricity continues to flow until a switch is opened or the energy source is exhausted.

Sometimes, in a hydraulic system (your home's plumbing, for example), a loud report somewhere back in the pipes will result when the water is shut off suddenly. This condition is called "water hammer." When the faucet was open, water flowed as a long line of traffic would. When the faucet was shut off, all of the moving water as far back as the source piled up. To this pressure was added the force from the momentum of the water, and a loud "ping" resulted when this flow "bounced back" into the system. In some cases, this bounce may have been sufficiently great to burst the pipes.

Roughly, this happens when the current in an electromagnetic coil is terminated suddenly, as it is in electric watches. The current has inertia and will tend to continue and to "bounce back" in somewhat the same way. Because it cannot either continue or return, a spark leaks off, burning and reducing the contacts, with the resulting damage we have already described.

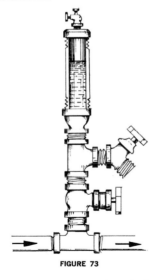

FIGURE 73

In the hydraulic system, plumbers overcome "water hammer" by providing an air chamber (*Figure 73*) to absorb and dissipate the shock of increased pressure. Water under extra pressure enters this appendage and compresses the air in it until an equilibrium is attained between the two forces. Then, slowly, the water distributes its pressure along the entire length of the pipe system.

In electrical systems, extra voltage which would burst off as a spark is channeled into a condenser or a capacitor of some sort. The resistance of a condenser to the backsurge of current is lower than the resistance of the air gap between the parted contacts, and the energy goes to the condenser where it is stored. Finally, it is dissipated along a small path from the condenser to the movement, or to the intake end of the coil. This all takes place in the smallest fraction of a second, but it is slow enough by electrical standards.

USED IN SWISS ELECTRIC

An instance of spark suppression can be seen in the Swiss electric watch, Landeron cal. 4750. Figure 74 is a schematic diagram of the watch's electrical system. In this case, the spark-suppressing parts are a resistor (*G*) and a diode (*H*).

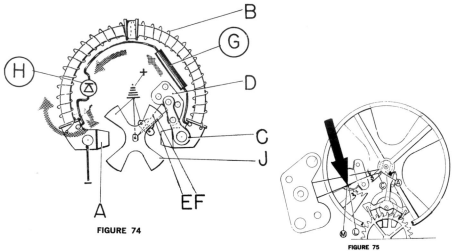

FIGURE 74

Schematic diagram of the electrical system in the Swiss watch. The normal flow of electricity through the coil is clockwise. A back-surge current, which results when the circuit is broken, tends to flow counter-clockwise through the coil, but is diverted through the resistor (G) and diode (H) to enter the coil in the normal direction, from the left. The current is absorbed and dissipated without sparking at contact points.

FIGURE 75

Contact points in the Swiss electric. When tab A parts from tip of spring C, plate M will spring away from beak L, breaking circuit. A spark would occur at this point (arrow) if resistor and diode were not present.

When the balance is in the position shown in Figure 75, the contacts are about to part. The metallic tab A on the balance will move past the tip of spring C in the counter-clockwise direction. This spring will break the circuit when it springs back from contact beak L at point M. Because of the coil and core, a spark would occur at the gap between M and L. But, as indicated in Figure 74, the surge of voltage is diverted through the resistor, which absorbs some of the back current, and into the diode.

A diode, of which we will learn more later, is an electronic valve to permit electricity to flow in one direction only. In Figure 74, the diode permits the current to flow in the direction shown by the arrows. This surge of current flows into the left hand side of the coil, where the energy is dissipated.

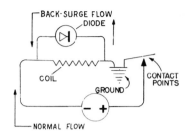

FIGURE 76

The Lip watch. The back-surge flow, which tends to enter the coil in the counter-clockwise direction, is diverted instead through the diode and re-enters the coil in the normal direction, where it is dissipated.

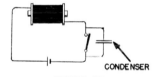

FIGURE 77

Use of a condenser is another way to suppress sparking. Extra current is temporarily absorbed by the device, and released at a rate slow enough to avoid a spark buildup.

The Lip electric watch suppresses sparking by a "contact diode." The system is schematized in Figure 76. As the balance revolves after energizing the electromagnets and receiving an impulse from them, certain contact points are parted. This opens the circuit, and a back-surge of current takes the path of least resistance through the contact-shielding diode instead of going through the coil. This diode is biased so that it allows current to flow in the direction shown by the arrow above it. The voltage then pushes the current along into the left part of the coil, where it is dissipated. The sparking that would have occurred at the air gap between the contacts is greatly suppressed.

In the Hamilton and German electrical watches, sparking is minimized because the electromagnetic coil is hollow.

Another way to reduce sparking is by means of a condenser or capacitor. Such a device stores an electric charge. It may consist of two thin electrical conductors side by side, separated by a thin insulating layer, and hooked up in parallel with the contacts, as shown by the arrow in Figure 77.

The energy that would result in a spark is led into the condenser. Sometimes, one of the conductors is grounded to allow a slower path for this surge current to dissipate.

RELAY CIRCUITS & GENERATOR PENDULUMS
REDUCE WEAR AND TEAR

Using relays, a balance or pendulum can swing without mechanical hinderance or electrical deterioration

We have seen that sparking and deterioration occur when contacts part. And we learned how to suppress this sparking.

One important implication of all this is that the secret of good electrical timekeeping is through a watch that can open and close circuits using no mechanical contacts whatever.

Many clocks (Kundo, Junghans-Ato-Hatot, etc.) operate this way. The only watch at present without mechanical contacts is the Accutron electronic timepiece. All of these use transistors in their circuits.

Timepieces with transistors and contact-less switching have one thing in common, generally missing from other clocks and watches. They use permanent magnets in conjunction with electromagnetic coils.

Long ago, it was predicted that since electricity can create magnetism, then perhaps magnetism can create electricity. It can.

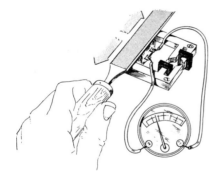
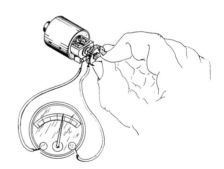

FIGURE 78

A simple generator may be constructed from a large magnetized file and the coil of a synchronous clock. When the file is passed over the coil, a galvanometer registers the quantity and direction of current.

FIGURE 79

Even a toy motor can become a generator because it contains the necessary elements: a coil and a magnet. By spinning the axle, a current registers on the meter.

MAKING A GENERATOR

To prove this, the watchmaker can set up another simple experiment, using an old, large file. Magnetize this in the hollow of a "demagnetizing" coil. Then, obtain the stator and coil of a synchronous clock, such as a Sessions or General Electric. Hook up the leads from this coil to those of a galvanometer or voltmeter as shown in Figure 78.

By moving the length of the magnetized file over the coil with rapid to-and-fro strokes, you will see a coincident movement of the meter needle, indicating a flow of electricity. The flow will be great if the file's movement is rapid, barely perceptible if the motion over the coil is slow.

We say that the magnet "generated" this current by passing over the coil. The speed and direction of the file's movement, the strength of the magnet and the type of coil determined the kind of current generated.

MOST GENERATORS SAME

Almost all electric generators work on the principle of magnets passing through or near to coils, or coils passing through or adjacent to magnets.

If we were to hook up a small direct current toy or clock motor, similar to that shown in figures 62-69, to a meter and spin the axle with our fingers, the meter would register a current (see figure 79). The direction and quantity of current would depend on the direction and strength of the spin. In one of the directions of spin, the meter will surge against the zero banking.

Thus, the direction of physical movement in our generator determines the direction of current. Specifically, the coils of wire cutting across magnetic lines of force generate the electricity, the direction of flow depending on from which direction the coil cuts these lines.

Instead of a meter, a flashlight bulb can be hooked up to our motor-become-generator. When spun, the generator will cause the tiny bulb to glow.

A CONTACT-LESS SWITCH

Now, if a current can be generated by a magnet passing near a coil (or a coil passing near a magnet), why can't a balance or pendulum containing a coil pass over or through a magnet generate electricity? Or, which is the same thing, a magnet mounted on a balance or pendulum, might pass over a coil and generate a current.

Such a current could operate a tiny switch or "relay" to

make a quick momentary circuit, which might be used to maintain the motion of the pendulum or balance.

The term relay is often used in electricity. It describes a system by which a small current triggers or releases a large stored voltage. A knowledge of the relay is important to an understanding of the electronic trigger—the transistor.

An example of the relay is the sending of signals over long distances by telegraph. The original electrical impulse needed to send a dot or dash across the country in one jump would use a tremendous amount of electricity and heavy equipment. An easier and simpler way is to have the small original impulse travel a number of short distances.

At way-stations along the route, this gradually-weakening impulse closes a second circuit which contains its own battery or energy source. This circuit sends out a fresh impulse to the next way-station, and so on.

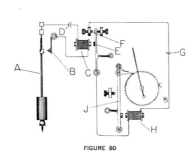

FIGURE 80

Another use of a relay system is the operation of many secondary clocks in a school, factory or public building by a single master clock. Figure 80 shows how this might be done.

The half-seconds pendulum A for a fine precision regulator is weight-driven or electrically impulsed. Its suspension has an electrical connection with battery D and electromagnetic coil C. Tab B is a contact.

CIRCUIT COMPLETED

When the pendulum swings from the left to right and touches contact B, a circuit is completed which energizes coil C. This coil magnetically attracts the contact button mounted on armature E, normally held back lightly by a helical spring.

When contact E moves to coil C, the space between F closes and completes a secondary circuit powered by cell G. This energizes coil H which pulls arm J toward it. The beak atop arm J moves over the racheted index wheel by one space. This wheel has 60 teeth, so that every movement of the half seconds pendulum indexes the wheel one unit, or one full second.

By providing additional relays to such a master clock, it is possible to impulse many secondary clocks, or rather, clock dials. On a smaller scale, a system of relays can be used in small clocks or watches.

It is even possible to propel the balance or pendulum itself without any visible physical contact, switching or wear. The coil or magnet could be situated on the balance or pendulum, and by passing over respectively, a magnet or coil, it might activate a relay, complete a circuit and release energy stored in a battery to further propel the balance or pendulum.

It might also be possible for such a relay system to trigger an independent or secondary circuit to move the indexing or dial train. In these ways, a balance or pendulum would be able to oscillate without mechanical interference from any part of the timepiece. It would be able to do its chronometric job and have no distracting influences or duties.

A PENDULUM GENERATOR

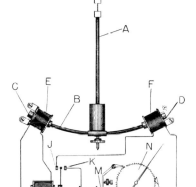

FIGURE 81

A set-up to achieve this is depicted in Figure 81. Pendulum A has a bob B of non-ferrous material, curved concentrically upon its point of suspension. Each end of this bob has a permanent magnet, C and D. The bob and magnets swing through hollow coils E and F, stationed at either side. This movement generates electric currents in the following succession:

As the pendulum swings to the left, it is travelling at its highest rate of speed when rod A is dead center, as shown, At this point, the left-hand permanent magnet has enough speed entering coil to generate a current sufficient to energize coil G and attract armature H. H is also a permanent magnet, normally too weak to be drawn to the coil's core at G. With the added electromagnetism generated by the pendulum's swing, however, it does move toward G, at the same time causing the contact above H to touch the contact J.

This completes the circuit through battery *I* and energizes coil *F* in such a way that its polarity is the same as magnet *D*. This repels the magnet in the right-to-left direction, implementing the swing of the pendulum.

At this point, the pendulum has swung as far left as it will go and begins to return in the left-to-right direction. It picks up speed, until again its greatest speed is at the dead center position. The magnet *C* enters coil *E* again, but from the opposite direction, creating a current in the opposite direction.

CURRENTS REVERSE

This current energizes coil *G* with the opposite polarity from before. The coil, therefore, repels magnet *H* and causes its upper point to make contact with *K* instead of *J*. This completes the circuit through coil *L*, battery *I*, and back to the spring contact upon which *H* is mounted.

While energized, coil *L*, draws armature *M* to it. A split second later, the generated current at *G* and *H* is terminated and the magnet *H* returns to the "open" position, allowing armature *M* to be drawn back by its helical spring. When *M* does go back, the beak mounted at its top will index the sixty-toothed rachet wheel *N*, causing the seconds hand mounted on the arbor of *N* to move one second of time forward.

Thus, with a half seconds pendulum the seconds hand is moved with every other swing of the pendulum, while the pendulum is impulsed once a second.

The important thing in such a system, however, is that the pendulum has no work to do, and makes no mechanical contacts. It swings freely, just keeping time.

ELECTRONIC VALVES PROVIDE THE ANSWER TO SPARK SUPPRESSION

The diode, key element in a transistor, allows current to flow in one direction only, removing the danger of short circuits

In discussing electricity and electronics, the term "amplify" often comes up. It refers to the use of an auxiliary or outside source of energy to make a weak electrical signal stronger. It's important to note that the outside source is set in action and controlled by the original weak impulse.

For example, the electrical relay shown in the diagram of

the magnetic pendulum (Figure 81) allowed a weak, induced current to close the circuit. As a result, a stronger current from a separate source (batteries) was tapped, augmenting the original impulse and thus "amplifying" it.

In electronic horology, a weak signal generated by a pendulum, balance, tuning fork or other oscillating device can be amplified by controlling the electrical power stored in a battery.

Previously, the sequence of events which caused the relay in a circuit containing a battery to produce amplification was spelled out in some detail. It was shown how the magnet-pendulum could induce a current (induction) by moving in a coil of insulated wire and how this current, although weak, could close a circuit in which a stronger impulse source (a battery) is present.

Figure 81 showed how a pendulum or any other oscillating device could be kept in continuous motion without any physical impulse-contact and how a dial train also could be indexed. However, in examples discussed previously, sparking would occur when electrical contact was broken. While spark suppressors could diminish this arcing they would not eliminate it entirely.

Mechanical switching is eliminated by using a transistor as an electronic escapement. In a conventional escapement, a larger power such as a spring or weight is stored and held in check by the lock of the escape tooth on the side of the pallet (jewel). Only a slight movement of the balance is needed to unlock the mainspring's power and impel the balance further.

The mechanical "transistor" or escapement thus consists of a stored power source, the mainspring, which is held in critical check by the escapement lock. The mainspring is released by the comparatively weak unlocking force of this balance.

In the electronic circuit, a large source of ready-to-release power, generally a battery, is held in check by an open "switch." Earlier, it was explained how it's possible for a small amount of electrical energy to close a switch and release a greater (stored) surge of electrical energy. In horology, the transistor is the valve, gate or escapement which allows this chain of events to take place without any visible moving part making or breaking electrical contacts.

DIODE: AN ELECTRONIC VALVE

Before attempting to explain how this is possible, it's as well to examine the basic principles of the transistor and how it works. Transistors will be used more and more in horology.

We will attempt to explain the principles in simple terms so the watch maker may understand what the transistor can be expected to do and, in general, how it is done. A good text on transistors is — "Transistors, Information, Experiments, Applications, Bureau of Naval Personnel. NAVPERS, 92387A, March, 1962. Supt. of Documents, U. S. Govt. Prtg. Office, Wash. 25, D. C.

The basis for the transistor is the diode, an electronic device or valve which allows current to flow in one direction only. It is composed of materials such as silicon or germanium.

In their pure state as crystals, no electrical current can flow through these materials. In fact, when these crystals are pure, they make excellent insulators. To permit them to conduct a current, small amounts of "impurities" are added. These impurities produce a condition which makes positive (+) or negative (—) charges available to carry current. Specific quantities of impurities are added to the crystals depending on the type and amount of current they will carry. If, for example, antimony is added to the crystal, negatively charged current carriers are made available.

The diode consists of two sections. Impurities introduced into one section produce negative current carriers; different types of impurities introduced to the other section produce positive current carriers.

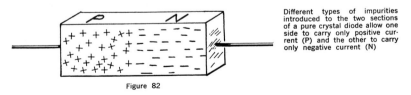

Different types of impurities introduced to the two sections of a pure crystal diode allow one side to carry only positive current (P) and the other to carry only negative current (N)

Figure 82

Figure 82 shows a diode in simplified form. The left-hand section contains impurities which will produce carriers of positive current. Thus, it is marked P. The right-hand section contains impurities producing negative current carriers. Thus, it is marked N. For further identification, the positive and negative sides may be marked plus (+) and minus (—) respectively. Connected to the sides of this diode are wires which could be connected electrically to a power source such as a battery.

AN EASY TEST

Suppose we try a simple experiment, using a diode (either an F-2, General Transistor or an International Rectifier S.D. 91A type with ratings, approximate 100 V, 750 m/a), a 1½ volt flashlight bulb and a one-cell battery.

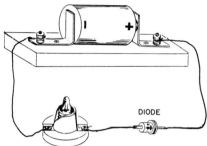

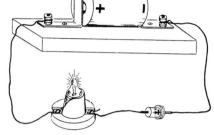

Figure 83

When the plus side of the battery is joined to the minus side of the diode and the minus side of the battery to the plus side of the diode the lamp does not light, indicating lack of current

Figure 84

Reverse the battery position shown in Fig. 83 so that plus sides of battery and diode are joined to plus and minus sides to minus. The lamp then lights, indicating a flow of current

These are connected in series with the diode (Figure 83) so that the plus side of the battery is connected to the negative side of the diode and the positive side of the diode is connected to the flashlight bulb. The wiring should then continue from the bulb to the negative side of the battery.

The bulb does not light up. This indicates that when connected in this manner almost no current passes through the diode. Now, reverse the battery in its holder (as in Figure 84) so that the plus side of the battery is connected to the bulb and through it to the plus side of the diode, the negative side of the battery is connected to the negative side of the diode. The bulb now lights up, proving that current will pass through the diode in one direction but not the other.

To understand this movement of current examine Figures 85A and 85B, remembering that like polarities repel and unlike polarities attract. When we connected the negative side of the battery to the positive half of the diode, the positive current carriers in the diode were attracted by the negative charge on the battery and rushed to the edge-end of the diode.

Likewise, on the other half of the diode, the negative current carriers were attracted to the positive terminal of the battery. This is shown in figure 85A in which a meter instead of a lamp indicates current flow. Thus, there were no current carriers in area A to serve as a conduit for the passage of current and so the current was blocked.

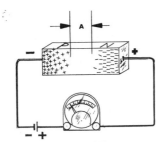

Figure 85A

Like polarities repel, unlike polarities attract. The battery's plus and minus charges, in effect, attract unlike current carriers in the diode to its outer edges eliminating carriers from area A (Fig. 85A), thus blocking the circuit.

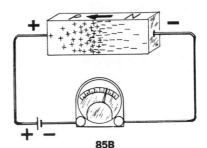

85B

By reversing the battery, carriers in the diode are forced towards each other to form a continuous current flow through the diode that establishes an electrical circuit (Fig. 85B)

Next, in Figure 85B, the battery was reversed so that its positive lead was connected to the half of the diode containing positive current carriers and the negative lead connected to the diode section containing negative current carriers.

In this condition, the positive current from the battery caused the positive current carriers in the diode (section P) to be repelled toward the junction between the two halves of the diode. On the other side of the diode (section N), the negative current carriers were being repelled by the battery's negative current.

In this condition, the junction between the two halves of the diode was "soaked" with current carriers of both polarities and the positive current from the battery thus could pass into the P section through the junction and continue in an electrical circuit. The negative carriers likewise had an uninterrupted path through the junction and could also complete the circuit, as shown in the meter reading.

SPARK SUPPRESSOR

The same test or experiment can be conducted using an ohmmeter instead of a light bulb. The ohmmeter will register a high resistance in one direction and a low resistance when the diode is reversed, proving that the diode can serve as a valve which allows current to pass in one direction and not the other.

Now it should be easier to understand the diode's role as a spark suppressor. Examine again Figures 74 and 76. When the current reverses itself and its polarity, the diode will allow this current to pass through and dissipate itself through the

72

energizing coil. But, when the current is required to go through the energizing coil, the diode blocks any attempt by the current to take a short-cut (circuit) from the battery to the contact.

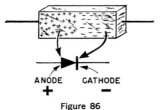

ANODE   CATHODE
+   **—**

Figure 86

Identifying symbols of the diode are an arrow the anode, and a black bar, the cathode. Electrons flow towards the anode (P) and flow from the cathode (N)

The electronic symbol for the diode is shown in Figure 86. The symbol is composed of an arrow head touching a short black bar. These two parts of the symbol represent the two parts of the diode. The arrow is called the *anode* and the black bar is called the *cathode*.

The anode is the electrode *towards* which the electrons flow. It is also called the positive electrode and corresponds to the P section. The cathode is the negative electrode *from* which the stream of electrons flows. It corresponds to the N section of the diode.

THE TRANSISTOR — HOW IT WORKS
AND WHAT IT DOES

Without sparking, this minute device can be used as an electronic switch to turn on or off the current which drives the watch mechanism

As explained earlier, the basis for the transistor is the diode, an electronic device or valve which allows current to flow in one direction only. Now, we want to consider in detail the transistor itself.

The transistor must be used when we want an electronic escapement capable of triggering an auxiliary source of current. In essence, the transistor consists of two diodes placed end-to-end and sharing a common center section. This is shown in figure 87.

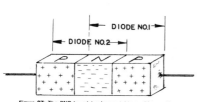

Figure 87: The PNP transistor has outside positive sections and a negative center. In effect, unit is two overlapping diodes.

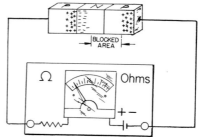

Figure 88: Repelling and attracting forces of ohmmeter's positive (left) and negative (right) leads draw current carriers from transistor's center, causing a circuit blocking void.

73

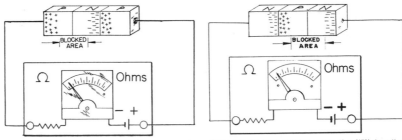

Figure 89: Even if the ohmmeter's leads are reversed a void still must be created because the outside transistor sections are of the same current carrying polarities.

Figure 90: The same situation exists if a NPN (negative-positive-negative) transistor is substituted for the PNP. A void through which current cannot pass again is created.

There are two types of transistor: (1) the PNP with two outside P (positive) sections and an N (negative) center section and (2) the NPN in which these outside sections contain negative current carriers and the middle contains positive current carriers.

Here we repeat another key statement which should make it easier to follow the electrical circuits described in this article: like polarities repel and unlike polarities attract. This basic fact cannot be repeated too often.

A NEW EXPERIMENT

If we connect an ohmmeter (an ammeter with its own internal battery) to a PNP transistor (Fig. 88) so that the positive lead (+) from the ohmmeter is connected to one position (P or +) section of the transistor and the negative lead (—) of the ohmmeter to the other positive (P or +) section of the transistor, there is no flow of current.

A study of the diagram should make the reason apparent. When the connection was made, the positive (+) charge from the ohmmeter repelled the positive current carriers in the left-hand section of the transistor toward the junction with the center section. Then, in turn, these positive carriers attracted the negative current carriers in the transistor's center section.

At the same time, the ohmmeter's negative charge attracted the positive current carriers in the right-hand section of the transistor to that section's outer edge. As a result a void through which no current could flow was created in the transistor. That area now is considered an insulator.

Even should we reverse the ohmmeter leads (Fig. 89), feeding a (+) charge from the ohmmeter battery to the contacts we had previously fed a (—) charge and vice versa, the same situation would exist since both outside transistor sections are of the same current carrying polarity. Hence, the empty section of the PN junction would be void of current carriers necessary to provide a path for a current. Thus current would be blocked.

Now let us try the same procedure with an NPN transistor as shown in figure 90. The outside sections of such a device contain some current carriers of negative polarity. When the negative side (—) of the ohmmeter is connected to one of the N's of the transistor, the current carriers in the transistor will be repelled by the like polarity of the ohmmeter's battery charge and crowd the area of its junction with the center P section. This part would normally be good for the passage of a current.

However, when the (+) lead of the ohmmeter is connected to the other N part of the transistor, current carriers here will be drawn away from the right part of the transistor's PN junction and a void, insulating area will be created. This is shown in figure 90.

Therefore, the transistor as it is pictured here cannot conduct a current through it. The difficulty lies in the fact that part of its junction (center section) develops an area void of current carriers when it is connected as shown.

AUXILIARY POWER

It becomes clear that if current is to flow through the transistor this void area must be filled with current carriers derived from an independent source.

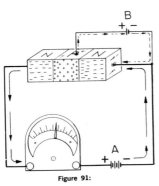

Figure 91:

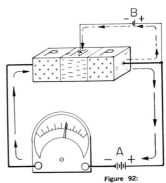

Figure 92:

Figure 91 shows how the unblocking is accomplished by connecting a small, *outside source of current* (battery B) to the blocked area and completing a circuit as though part of the transistor were a diode. In other words, applying a small voltage across the right two-third section (diode part of the transistor) so that the polarities of this battery would repel the current carriers towards the void areas.

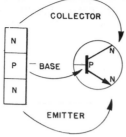

COLLECTOR

N

P — BASE

N

EMITTER

Figure 93: Schematic drawing of transistor's symbol. When arrow points away from base and toward circle, this identifies NPN transistor.

In this case, the positive terminal of the small battery (B) is connected to the section of the transistor containing P carriers, and the N part of this battery is attached to the section with N carriers. In this instance, the P carriers are driven into the mid-section of the transistor and provide a path between the other two sections. The other terminal of the small battery B repels the N carriers in the N section of the transistor to which it is connected and a path is provided for the current from the larger battery A to pass through all sections of the transistor.

Introduction of a small outside power source would be equally effective in completing an electrical circuit with a PNP transistor (Fig. 92).

To assist passage of a current through the mid-section of the transistor, this section generally is made narrower than the outside ends, thus providing a shorter path through the area once the flow of electricity is started.

This description of the transistor and the diode does not go deeply into the theory of these devices, but it should be sufficient to enable the watchmaker to understand what they do and, to some extent, how they do it. The use of transistors in horology should become clearer.

THE TRANSISTOR AT WORK

This ability to hold in check a large source of energy until a small current is applied to the mid-section of the transistor is important. It allows the transistor to be used as a switch to turn on and off a larger, stronger electrical impulse without involving sparking or any moving parts.

For example, when a pendulum is composed of a magnet, (Fig. 81), and this magnet-pendulum swings close to a coil, it could generate a small current. Although this induced current would be weak, if fed into the mid-section of a transistor it could distribute enough current carriers to unblock a void

76

area in the transistor.

With the void unblocked, current then could pass through the transistor from the main battery and complete a circuit. This circuit could energize a coil to impel further the oscillating device used—whether it was a pendulum, balance, tuning fork or other device. In fact, this basic principle is used in modern transistor clocks as well as in the Accutron.

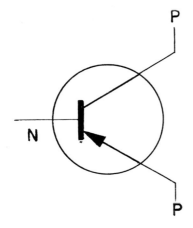

P

N

P

Figure 94: In this symbolic drawing, the arrow points to and touches the base, identifying PNP transistor.

FACTS TO REMEMBER

The transistor's symbol in schematic drawings is shown in figure 93. The mid-section to which the auxiliary triggering current is fed is called the *base*. The other two leads are called the *emitter* and the *collector*. The following facts and definitions also should be noted:

The emitter is so called because it emits current carriers.

The emitter part of the transistor symbol always is identified with an arrow.

The collector is so called because it collects the current carriers which emit from the emitter.

When the arrow points away from the base and toward the circle (Fig. 93) this identifies an NPN transistor.

When the arrow points to and touches the base (Fig. 94) this identifies a PNP transistor.

Instead of a symbol, the letters EBC (emitter, base and collector) sometimes are used.

Transistors come in many shapes, sizes and ratings for electrical capacities and performances. Larger ones, logically, are built to handle stronger electrical currents. Tiny ones, engineered to handle smaller signals, are used in watches. However, regardless of their size, all transistors have three leads, one each for the emitter (E), base (B) and collector (C) connections.

The transistor has fairly standard features to identify these three leads. For example, in a transistor of the type shown in

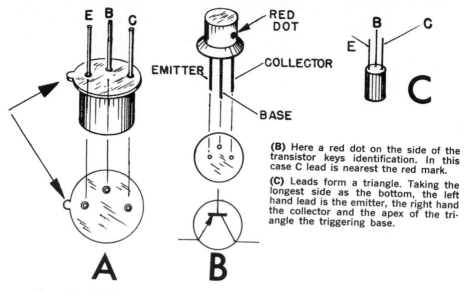

(B) Here a red dot on the side of the transistor keys identification. In this case C lead is nearest the red mark.

(C) Leads form a triangle. Taking the longest side as the bottom, the left hand lead is the emitter, the right hand the collector and the apex of the triangle the triggering base.

Figure 95: (A) Letters E, B and C denote emitter, base and collector. In Fig. A a small tab on the side of the transistor establishes identification. The E lead always is nearest the tab.

figure 95A a slight tab extending from the flange indicates that the pin nearest to it is the *emitter*. Continuing the sequence, the center pin is the *base* and the pin farthest from the tab is the *collector*.

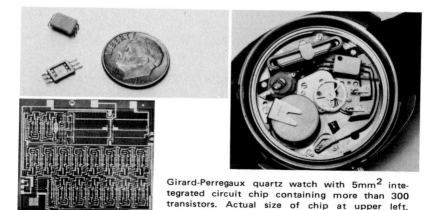

Girard-Perregaux quartz watch with 5mm^2 integrated circuit chip containing more than 300 transistors. Actual size of chip at upper left, enlarged view below.

MARKS OF IDENTITY

In figure 95B another method is used to identify the leads. Where design of the transistor prohibits use of an extending tab on the flange a red dot is placed on the cylindrical portion of the transistor casting.

In this case, the dot identifies the nearest pin as the *collector*. Thus, the pin farthest from the dot is the *emitter* and once again the center pin is the *base*.

Notice that a triangle is formed by the placement of the pins (Fig. 95C). Taking the longest side of the triangle as the bottom, the left pin is the emitter, the right pin is the collector and the pin at the apex of the triangle is the triggering base.

Included earlier, was a section on relays, spark suppressors and the induction of a current by passing a magnet over a coil. The section was illustrated with diagrams. With the additional information provided. Perhaps now you can change these diagrams to eliminate all contacts and substitute diodes and transistors for sparkless, contactless switching of currents.

A TRANSISTORIZED CLOCK

Now that we know something about the transistor, we are ready to examine a timepiece which uses this tiny switch. Let's find one that uses a transistor in its simplest application.

Clock and transistor. This photo shows clock and cylindrical housing that surrounds the curved pendulum rod. The housing contains all elements necessary to propel the pendulum yet, because it is transistorized, this source of power never contacts the rest of the clock. The 1.5 volt battery will last at least five years.

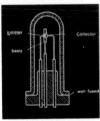

Figure is a cross section of the clock's transistor.

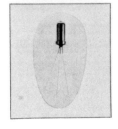

Bottom photo shows the transistor. It is 5 mm in diameter, 15 mm long.

The Kundo transistor clock (see photograph), imported by Fred J. Koch, 1115 Broadway, New York, is such a timepiece. Figure 96 diagrams the clock before it was transistorized; figure 97 shows it incorporating a transistor.

The main part in either clock is the pendulum, suspended in the usual manner with spring and chocks. The pendulum rod is Invar and is threaded to support the adjustable regulating weight J. This can set the clock to an accuracy of a few seconds per day. A yoke cradles curved rod F and is fastened by set-screws in the rear. The curved rod swings freely through hollow coil G. The right side of rod F is hollow and carries a short rod magnet of high intensity.

Battery H supplies power. It is flat, fastened to the underside of the clock case platform.

In figure 96 the negative (—) terminal is connected to coil G, and the positive (+) terminal is grounded to the movement to complete the circuit when the proper contact is made.

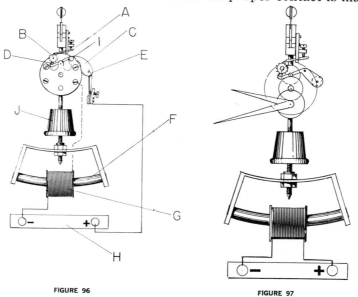

FIGURE 96

FIGURE 97

Electric clock without transistor must have a circuit-breaking mechanism. Sparking, "leakage" and deterioration result at point E as a circuit "makes" or "breaks."

Same clock, transistorized, has fewer moving parts, no sparking. All electrical components except the battery are contained in the coil unit, as shown in figure 98.

A CIRCUIT WITH CONTACTS

Completion of the circuit in this older model is accomplished by electrical contacts when the pendulum swings in the clockwise, right-to-left direction. Indexing lever A, near the top of the pendulum, intercepts a tooth atop index wheel B and moves it one division.

Nestled between two of the lowest teeth on the index wheel is a little roller *D* mounted on the contact lever *C* which is pivoted at *I*. When the index wheel turns, its lowest teeth push roller *D* down and cause the right side of lever *C* to see-saw up. A small pin on the lever's tail touches contact spring *E* to complete the electrical circuit.

The current now flows from the battery into coil *G*. The coil becomes an electromagnet and its magnet further in the right-to-left direction.

As the pendulum swings further along, the contacts are broken after roller *D* drops into the next recess between teeth and the pendulum swings back freely until the cycle repeats i.e., when the pin on lever *C* again touches contact spring *E*. The screws on *E* provide the contacts with a fine adjustment.

In figure 97 the clock is much simpler. There are no electrical contacts, and both battery leads are connected directly to the coil. Lever *C* is also somewhat simpler. Its tail is weighted to supply just enough pressure for roller *D* to remain between the lower two teeth of the index wheel. This roller, and lever *C*, now serve only to position the index wheel and to provide a "jump" action when a tooth passes the crest of the roller.

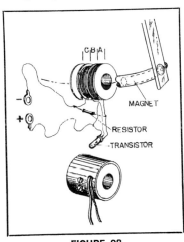

FIGURE 98

Coil unit is essentially the stator (fixed) part of a generator with its own off-on switch (transistor). Compartment **A** houses the transistor-triggering coil, **B** holds the main, pendulum-impulsing coil, **C** the transistor and a resistor. Current is created in coil **A**, then **B** as magnet in pendulum passes through in one direction. Lower sketch shows how three elements appear in brass shell.

TRANSISTOR TRIGGERS CIRCUIT

The pendulum is impulsed electronically. All components for this are sealed in the coil unit's outer shell. They are the transistor, a transistor-triggering coil, an impulsing coil and a resistor. There are three sections to the coil unit (figure 98) : the triggering coil *A* allows the transistor to release current from the battery; the strong impulsing coil *B* propels the bar magnet in the pendulum; compartment *C* houses the transistor and resistor. The whole unit is encapsulated in a brass shell and appears as shown in the lower sketch of figure 98.

The pendulum is started by hand. When it swings from the

left to the right, no electrical action occurs. The polarity of the induced current, generated by the magnet moving through the triggering coil, happens to be opposite that required to trigger the transistor.

THE CIRCUIT COMPLETES

When the pendulum re-enters the coil in the right-to-left direction, its encased magnet enters the trigger part of the coil (A) and induces a weak current of the proper polarity and intensity. This goes to the base of the transistor. The transistor releases the large battery current to the impulsing section of the coil (B), which further attracts the magnetic part of the pendulum bar. As the pendulum continues in this direction, the magnet leaves the coil and current ceases to flow to the transistor's base. This terminates the transistor's operation for the cycle and thus shuts off the large battery current. Since there are no mechanical contacts, no sparking takes place.

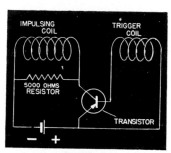

FIGURE 99

Resistor is placed across impulsing coil to absorb back-surge EMF when impulsing coil switches off.

When the battery current ceases abruptly, the magnetic field in the coil collapses and a back EMF (electro - magnetic force) arises. To avoid any back-surge towards the transistor and to dissipate this EMF so that the termination of the pendulum impulse is sudden and complete, a resistor is placed across the impulsing coil. It is a refinement of the electronic action and is schematized in figure 99.

INDEXING

The mechanical action is rather simple, all of it directed to moving the hands. Each clockwise movement of the pendulum indexes a tooth which is enmeshed with a train of wheels (actually, a part of the dial train). The 1/3-second pendulum oscillates 180 times per minute and indexes 90 times per minute.

The indexing mechanism is shown in figures 100 and 101. A is the indexing wheel, B the indexing lever, C a retaining pawl and F the roller at rest, nestled between two teeth of the indexing wheel. The pawl is weighted at C to provide the necessary tension for roller F. C pivots at its center. Adjusting screws D and E regulate the depth and arc of indexing lever B

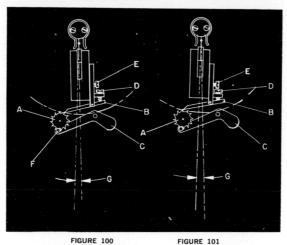

FIGURE 100   FIGURE 101

Indexing adjustment. Raise or lower screw **D** so that indexing
lever **B** gathers but one tooth. Depth of lever's arc is changed by
turning screw **D** or loosening screw **E** to raise or lower chock upon
which **D** and **B** are mounted.

as it engages index wheel A. The half-arc of the pendulum
necessary to index the wheel is represented by G.

To adjust the clock's indexing mechanism, raise or lower
screw D so that indexing lever B gathers but one tooth, regardless of the pendulum arc's width. The roller beneath provides part of the indexing as the tip of a lower tooth pushes
past the crest of the roller. The depth of the arc should be
such that lever B barely misses the tooth in front of the one
being intercepted. The arc of the indexing lever can also be
adjusted by loosening screw E and lowering the chock upon
which D and B are mounted.

LUBRICATION AND CHECKING

Little can go wrong with the clock mechanically since there
are few wheels. These are driven in reverse compared to
wheels in mainspring clocks; therefore, there is practically
no pivot or bushing hole wear. The main pivot holes are jeweled. Oil should be used sparingly and no oil should be placed
on the index wheel or roller, or on the indexing unit.

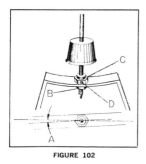

FIGURE 102

Lock pendulum for carrying by tightening spring-loaded screw in hole of nut
D. Bird's-eye view of pendulum yoke
reveals it is off center **(A)**. Adjustment
is made by loosening nut **B**, aligning
yoke, retightening.

The pendulum adjustment is shown in figure 102. When the clock must be moved, raise the pendulum by hand a few milimeters and thread the spring-loaded screw, located on the back stand of the clock, into the hole of nut D. This locks the pendulum for carrying and prevents damage to the vulnerable suspension spring.

The clock must be stationed upright, using the four uprighting screws in the corner of the base. The pendulum's curved bar should swing straight through the center of the coil. Should it not, loosen nut B below the pendulum yoke, and straighten the pendulum. Be careful not to kink the suspension spring. Grasp nut C firmly to loosen nut B. Be certain that threaded hole D is in the front position as it must be square to the axis of the spring-loaded locking screw.

Make certain that all electrical connections are tight and that all contacts have been checked. The consumption of this

Power source of the Kundo clock is a single battery, more properly termed a monocell. It is designed to run the clock for a full 5 years.

FIGURE 103

clock is about ¾ of an ampere-hour annually. The circuit permits this cell to be used long after the same cell on electric clocks would have become useless, because in a transistor clock the current is turned on only when needed.

Measure the battery (a monocell of 1.5 volts) with a high-impedance voltmeter. As soon as the pressure falls below 1.1 volts, the battery should be changed.

THE SEMCA TRANSISTORIZED BALANCE CLOCK

Our study of transistors in timepieces continues, using a balance clock as an example

We learned that a pendulum containing a magnet, by passing through a stationary, hollow coil, can 1) generate a small current to trigger a transistor, which 2) releases a strong electrical current stored in a monocell, in order to 3) impulse a pendulum without switches or sparking.

In this article, and the one which follows, we will see that this same sequence can impel a balance.

Our model is the AN transistor clock, a product of France's La Generale Horlogere (JAZ). Its movement is shown in Figure 104. The unit is small and light; in its transparent

The movement. **A** is the coil combination, **B** the transistor, **C** is a condenser and **D** is the fiber plate on which all stationary electronic parts are fastened.

FIGURE 104

casing it measures about 2¼ in. square and weighs less than 3 oz. It is recognized by the disc-shaped coil, a condenser and a transistor fitted to a removable, fiber plate. We may refer to such a self-contained assembly as an electrical "module." It is designed to be replaced as a unit if only one of its components breaks down.

ELECTRICAL COMPONENTS

Figure 105 is a drawing of this module. It is easily taken from the movement without disturbing the balance by removing two screws. The module is pulled out past the long neck of the balance via a channel in the fiber plate. This is indicated by a dashed line.

The coil (*A*) measures 10.5 mm by 3.5 mm and consists of two separate windings, not differentiated in this drawing. One is the transistor-triggering coil; the other is the balance-im-

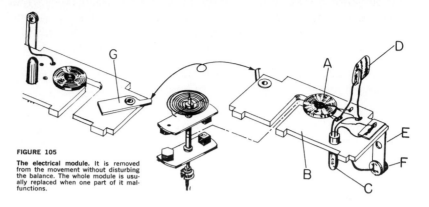

pulsing coil. The transistor (C) measures 5 mm by 15 mm. Item D is a condenser and E the hole through which one of the screws fastens the module to the movement. Tab F is the electrical contact to a battery lead.

The top drawing in figure 105 shows fiber plate B in the downside-up position. This reveals amplitude control piece G. The hole in the eyelet of this piece positions the other movement-fastening screw.

In the Kundo clock, a permanent magnet, mounted on the pendulum, generated a small voltage when it passed through the coil. This neutralized the "blocked" area at the base of the transistor and released a major current through the circuit. The current pulsing through another coil, magnetizing it. Finally, this magnet pulled against the permanent magnet in the pendulum and kicked the pendulum along in its arc.

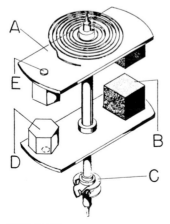

BALANCE DOES SAME

The Semca clock also uses permanent magnets, but they are on a balance.

The balance is shown in detail by figure 106. It is basically a long staff on which are mounted two aluminum plates (A). On the inside of these plates are two strong alnico magnets (B) of opposite polarities.

Counterpoising these magnets are two eccentrically mounted hexagonal nuts (D), friction-

FIGURE 106

Balance and staff. The balance swings back and forth, straddling the stationary coil (not shown here).

fastened by rivets (E). Poising the balance is accomplished by twisting these nuts so that they are, in effect, closer or further from the center of the staff. "Escapement" (C) indexes an escape wheel and a train of gears.

Start the clock by twisting the balance. A push-button arrangement or a twist of the whole clock does this. The motion causes the magnets which straddle the coil to induce a light voltage in the coil's transistor-triggering winding. This small voltage causes the transistor to release the larger battery voltage to the coil's impulsing winding and turns the coil into an electromagnet strong enough to attract the permanent magnets on the balance.

Notice that the coil is hollow. When the magnets pass over this area, no current is generated in the transistor-triggering winding. The transistor base is again deadened and this terminates the current from the battery through the impulsing coil. The balance now continues by momentum until arrested by the resilient hairspring. The balance then reverses its direction. When its magnets approach the flat coil the cycle repeats. The magnetic sequence works in both directions.

SCHEMATIC EXPLANATION

The electronic sequence will be made clear by schematic drawings (figures 107 and 108). In figure 107, M represents the impulsing winding of the coil. One end of this coil connects with the negative (—) battery terminal and the other end connects with the collector (C) of the transistor. The emitter (E) of the transistor connects with the positive (+) terminal of the battery.

No current can pass between the emitter and the collector (to complete the circuit through coil M) because of the blocked area of the base (B) of the transistor. To neutralize the base at the right moment and allow current to flow between E and C, coil R is connected between E and B. (Figure 108 shows how coil R is sandwiched in with coil M. R is represented by the dotted line.) When the magnets pass over the edge of this coil, an induced current is created which then flows between E and B. This small current "unlocks" the base of the transistor which then permits the large, stored battery current to flow between E and C and through coil M.

Coil M becomes a magnet with poles opposite in charge to the permanent magnets on the balance (N and S, figure 108). Thus the balance is attracted once the circuit completes.

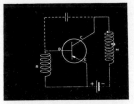

FIGURE 107

Schematized circuit. Current flows through coil **M** after coil **R** generates enough current to "unlock" the base **(B)** of the transistor, allowing battery current to flow between **E** and **C**. Dotted line hooks into a condenser to make current build-up sudden and uniform.

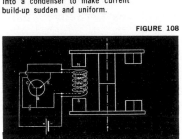

FIGURE 108

Coil **M and coil R** are sandwiched together. The magnets (**N** and **S**) on the balance straddle the coils inducing current in coil **R** (dotted line) and receiving an electromagnetic impulse from coil **M** (solid line).

CONDENSER HELPS OUT

The condenser is a device to store electrons. It is also called a capacitor. When the balance magnets pass over the triggering coil, current is built up too gradually for isochronal purposes. The electromagnetic impulse to the balance should be sudden and uniform. When properly charged, therefore, the condenser sends the full charge through the transistor base and this allows the transistor to unleash the battery's power in a business-like manner.

Figure 108 shows how the two coils are wound together, one within the other, each performing its own job independently. As you study the drawing, try to see how, as the balance arms pass through, coil *R* triggers the transistor and coil *M* delivers a magnetic impulse to the balance assembly.

The indexing unit of the Semca clock is a kind of reciprocating worm drive, reminiscent of the Jaegar auto clock devices. This process differs from the indexing of mainspring timepieces in that the pinions drive the wheels. Such an arrangement results in little torque or side friction. Motion is translated from the balance wheel through collar-like pallets which index the teeth of an escape wheel, setting off a train of gears.

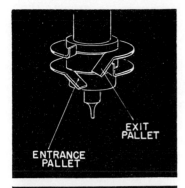

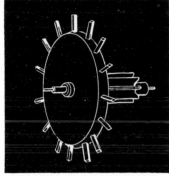

FIGURES **109** (top) and **110** show the escape mechanism: the pallets collaring the lower part of the balance staff, and the escape wheel which is indexed by the pallets.

INDEXING MECHANISM

The main components of the unit, illustrated in Figure 109, are the pallets, set in grooves around the lower part of the balance staff. They are essentially two thin discs, each with a downward slanted ramp at one end and a bent up tab at the other. The two ramps face each other, positioned to receive the tooth of the adjacent escape wheel, which is shown in Figure 110. These teeth radiate from the wheel like diamond-shaped pins. The wheel is made of a teflon-type plastic, requiring no oil. The pallets work at right angles to the plane of rotation of the escape wheel.

The sequence of motion is illustrated in Figure 111. The tooth to be indexed stands out here in solid black. In 1, as the balance shaft turns in the direction of the arrow (counter-clockwise), the tooth is gathered by the lower, or entrance pallet and lifted up the inclined plane of the ramp until it rests on the flat surface,

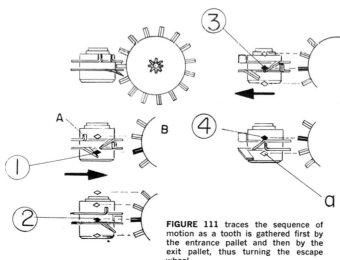

FIGURE **111** traces the sequence of motion as a tooth is gathered first by the entrance pallet and then by the exit pallet, thus turning the escape wheel.

as in 2. The tooth remains at this level while the balance continues to turn by momentum until the hairspring arrests the balance and returns it in the clockwise direction shown by the arrow in 3. This same tooth is now gathered by the upper, or exit pallet and lifted up the ramp until it again rests on a horizontal surface, as in 4. Notice here that the next tooth (*a*) is in the same position as the black tooth in 1. As the balance reverses once more and travels counter-clockwise, the entrance pallet will gather up tooth *a* in the same manner. The escape wheel teeth will in turn revolve the gears of the movement.

Overwinding is prevented by tabs *A* and *B* (Figure 111, *1*), which act as precautionary backstops for the teeth. The escape wheel has no loose, free motion—only that initiated by the slanted ramps. The wheel is controlled by the light pressure of a brake plate upon the escape wheel arbor, much like that of a friction spring upon the sweep second pinion of a watch.

PRECISION ADJUSTMENTS

FIGURE 112

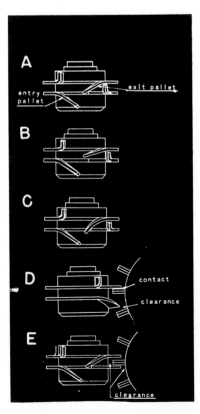

While the escapement is a simple mechanism, the position and angle of each pallet and its relationship to the escape wheel must be precise or butting and jamming will result. Examine the drawings in Figure 112. The exit pallet should be adjusted so that its lower tip is exactly aligned with the flat part of the entry pallet, as shown in *A*. If the tip of the ramp is too high (*B*) or too low (*C*) it will bump against a tooth, impeding the regulation of the movement and even stopping the balance. Bend the inclined ramp so that it coincides with the path of the escape tooth and gathers it up. Although these ramps are made of tempered steel, they can be manipulated easily with tweezers. To test the alignment, turn the balance slowly by hand until the ramp of the entrance pallet meets a tooth. Turn the balance

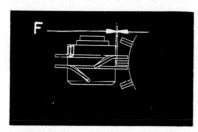

FIGURE 112 (CONT'D)

FIGURE 112 illustrates the need for precision adjustments to assure adequate clearance between pallets and escape teeth.

about one-eighth of a revolution further to bring the tooth to the top of the slope. Then turn the escape wheel in the opposite direction to make sure that this same tooth touches the bottom of the exit pallet (*D*).

There should be a clearance of about .10mm between the tip of the entry ramp and the next tooth on the escape wheel (*D*). If the pallet interferes with the tooth, its tip should be gently bent upward.

A minimum clearance of .10mm is needed between the balance and the escape wheel at the points shown in *E*. Check all 15 teeth for this measurement in case the wheel is mounted eccentrically. If the clearance is too small, as in *F*, adjust the cambered bracket (potence) on the back plate which carries the lower bearing of the balance.

The balance magnets should be free of any dust particles. These could interfere with the motion of the balance assembly when it passes through the narrow space around the coil. Also make certain that the wires to and from the coil are secured to the mounting plate with epoxy resin. The magnets should clear both sides of the coil by .2mm.

The brake plate, which prevents backlash of the escape wheel, should be adjusted so that its contact with the escape wheel arbor is sufficient but not too strong. The plate should contact the escape wheel pinion over a length of 2mm. Grease this area but keep escape teeth dry.

If the amplitude of the balance is too great, rebanking may cause the upturned tabs of the pallets to strike the escape teeth (Figure 109, A). Consequently an electrical brake is needed to keep the balance revolving in a 270° arc, which is most advantageous for isochronism. This device is a flat copper tongue, held friction tight upon the screw-hole eyelet. (See *G* in Figure 105). When the magnets pass over the tongue during their arc, they induce eddy currents in the piece of copper. These currents momentarily block the magnetic field between the magnets, thus inhibiting the motion of the balance. This braking effect is proportional to the extent that the tongue projects into the magnetic field. The tongue should be

91

rotated until it allows the balance three-fourths of a turn.

If the balance amplitude diminishes, however, another automatic control compensates. Since the balance moves less, the transistor remains in a conducting state longer and the period of time during which the current flows through the coil increases.

Once the balance system and the indexing unit are checked for precision, the movement can be adjusted for isochronism. If the movement gains when connected to a 1.3 volt battery, spread the regulator pins apart. If it loses time when tested with a fresh battery of 1.6 volts, move the hairspring toward the inside pin of the regulator. Always test the movement regulation at the 1.6 voltage after each adjustment. A new clock will keep time between 1.6 and 1.3 volts for two years, and, according to manufacturers, should remain accurate until the voltage falls to 1.2.

Some of the technical data concerning this movement are listed here:
Electrical consumption: Average 120 microamps.
Balance swing: 230° to 270°.
Temperature limits: Minus 20°C to 90°C (—22°F to 194°F).
Operating voltages: 1.6 down to 90 volts.
Coil M (Impulse coil, Figure 106): 2000 turns.
Thickness of impulse coil wire: 0.04 mm. (.0015 in.).
Resistance of impulse coil: 650 ohms.
Coil R (Triggering coil, Figure 106): 2000 turns.
Thickness of triggering coil wire: 0.04 mm. (.0015 in.).
Duration of current pulse of impulsing coil: .12 to 15 milliseconds.
Condenser: 0.025 microfarad.

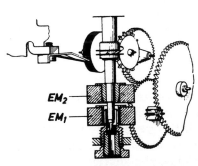

A movement made by the Junghans Company, in Germany, similar to the one we have been discussing, appears in Figure 113. However, we notice in this latter movement that attached to the balance shaft below the escapement is a collar magnet, EM_2. Facing this is another magnet, EM_1, attached to the lower pivot bushing, situated in the plate. These magnets repel each other, effecting a floating

FIGURE 113. A German version of the Semca uses opposing magnets (EM_1 and EM_2) to force the weight of the balance off the lower pivots.

balance with no strain or weight upon the lower pivot and low
er cap jewel.

FIGURE 114 (below) shows an exploded view of the Semca
balance movement to facilitate assembly of parts.

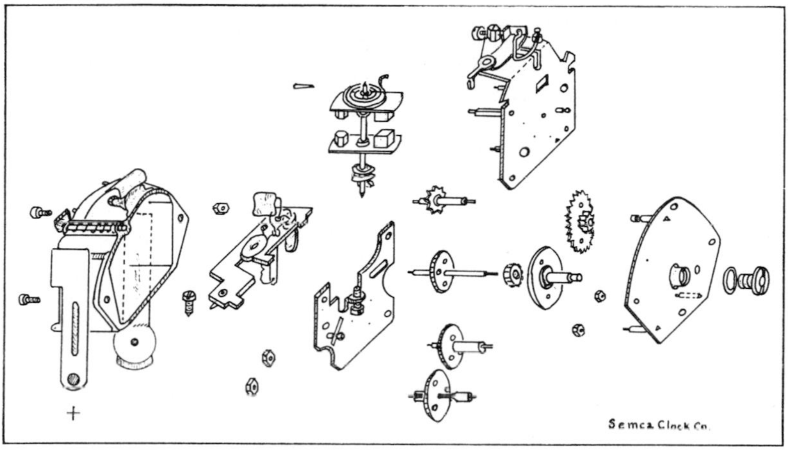

Semca Clock Co.

THE CAPACITOR'S ROLE IN TIMEPIECES

A tiny reservoir for electricity helps maintain an even impulse in the electronic clock or watch

Many electronic timepieces contain capacitors, which perform various necessary functions. Here, we shall discuss the
capacitor, its principles and characteristics, in preparation for
the series which will deal with the Accutron circuit and its
use of the capacitor.

In its simplest form, a capacitor is composed of two electrical conductors separated by an insulator called a *dielectric*.
This insulator may be waxed paper, mica, ceramic, air, or
even certain chemicals which will oppose the passage of an
electric current.

AIR AS A DIELECTRIC

Let us consider as an example two thin metallic plates,
closely facing each other. They are separated by an air gap
which provides insulation, acting as the dielectric in this case.
The plates are connnected in series with a battery, a switch,
and a *galvanometer*, or device to measure electric current, as
shown in Figure 115. The middle point on the dial of the

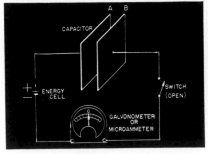

FIGURE 115

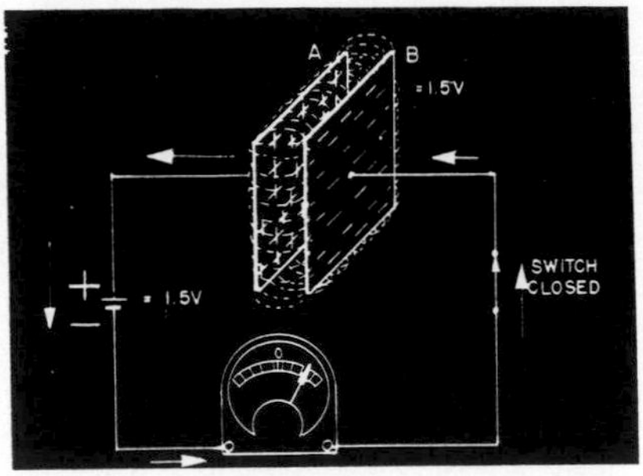

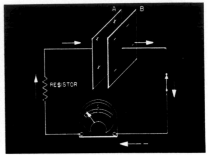

FIGURE 116

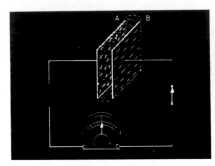

FIGURE 117

FIGURE 118

Figure 115 illustrates the circuit of a typical capacitor, plates A and B. Figure 116 shows the switch closed and the battery charging the plates. The charge is maintained in the capacitor, Figure 117, even when the battery is removed. When dielectric strain is relieved in Figure 118 by connecting the circuit without pressure exerted by the battery, the capacitor discharges.

galvanometer is zero; if current flows through this meter in one direction, the hand will deflect to the right, and if current flows in the opposite direction, it will point to the left.

By closing the switch, as in Figure 116, we cause current to flow from the negative pole of the battery around the circuit to plate B, which receives a negative charge. This places a strain on the dielectric, in pushing electrons against and off plate A and back to the positive terminal of the battery. Plate A thus has positive polarity. As the current flows from the negative to the positive pole through the circuit in Figure 116, we see the galvanometer pointing its hand to the right. The plates of the capacitor are being charged so that an electrostatic field is set up between them, as shown by the dotted lines. The opposite polarities of the plates store energy in the dielectric material between them.

94

PRESSURE SEEKS TO EQUALIZE

This action is similar to that exchanged between a bicycle tire and a small tank of compressed air. *Air is transferred from the source to the capacitor until the pressure of each is equalized.* When the air in the tire reaches the same pressure as the tank, air stops flowing between the two. Similarly, when the voltage (or pressure) stored in the capacitor becomes equal to that in the battery, current flow ceases. The galvanometer registers zero again and the capacitor is charged.

In Figure 117, the battery has been disconnected, opening the circuit. The capacitor will maintain its already charged voltage. But should we complete the circuit by substituting a resistor, coil, or other conductor in place of the battery, the negative charges on plate B would rush through the galvanometer back around to positive plate A, since the strain of pressure against the dielectric would be relieved. This is shown in Figure 118, where the meter is registering to the left side of the dial. The capacitor thus discharges and the current stored in the electrostatic field is exhausted.

QUANTITY OF CURRENT CAN CHANGE

The amount of electrical energy that the capacitor can contain depends on three things: the surface area of the plates, the distance between the plates, and the type of dielectric or insulating material separating the plates. If the surfaces facing each other are made larger, they will be able to store a greater amount of current for a given voltage. Furthermore, if the plates are closer together, they are akin to two magnets —their electrostatic attraction for each other is stronger and they are able to hold a larger charge. If the plates are so close that they touch, they will discharge. Therefore, insulating material is used.

Air is taken as a standard, with a *dielectric constant of 1*. Mica, waxed paper, and ceramic make better dielectrics and so have higher constant values. Since waxed paper has a dielectric constant of 6, changing a capacitor from one with air to a comparable one with waxed paper means that the unit will hold six times as much charge. This is due to the fact that electrical energy is stored in the dielectric's atomic structure.

We compared a capacitor to a bike tire accepting air from a compressor. The smaller the tire is, the more quickly it will fill to capacity, or, in the case of a capacitor , the faster it will charge. On the other hand, should too much pressure be applied, the tire would burst, and, a capacitor subjected to too great a voltage would cause a spark to jump between the plates, burning through the insulating dielectric and ruining the capacitor. The maximum voltage of the unit, beyond which sparking will occur, is called the *breakdown voltage*. This value sometimes appears on the unit and warns not to purposely exceed this load. The air space capacitor is an exception to this situation, as it would be self-healing.

APPLICATION TO TIMEPIECES

Capacitors for clocks and watches generally are of two types. One is composed of long thin strips of metal foil separated by dielectrics of waxed paper, as illustrated in Figure 119. Wire leads connect to the foil, and the unit rolls up to permit a large surface area to be condensed into a small, sturdy capacitor.

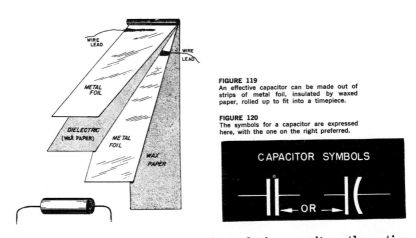

FIGURE 119
An effective capacitor can be made out of strips of metal foil, insulated by waxed paper, rolled up to fit into a timepiece.

FIGURE 120
The symbols for a capacitor are expressed here, with the one on the right preferred.

The other type is called an *electrolytic capacitor;* the action of a chemical such as a borax solution upon aluminum causes an extremely thin layer of aluminum oxide and oxygen gas to form on the surface of the metal. Thus, the aluminum plate becomes one pole of the capacitor and the borax solution the other. Because the coating of oxygen and aluminum oxide is not an electrical conductor, it becomes the dielectric. The aluminum can be folded or rolled to occupy a relatively small space. Because this chemical dielectric is so thin, the capacitance of the unit is very high. It is important to observe polarities as marked on the case, when connecting battery leads to the electrolytic capacitor, in order to prevent the unit from burning itself out by a wrong connection.

COMPENSATING MECHANISM

Capacitors have the ability to compensate for a change in voltage in the circuit. They are essentially reservoirs of electricity. Referring back to Figure 116, the charge in a capacitor will build up until it equals the charge of its source. As the difference in pressure between the capacitor and the battery lessens, the rate of flow slows down. The capacitor draws the most current when it is void of electricity. If the battery voltage should fall below that of the charged capacitor, part of this stored energy would flow back to the battery, just as a leak in the tire would cause more air to fill from the tank. Thus the capacitor, once charged, helps to maintain a constant voltage in the circuit. It is also able to accept a rise in voltage by being additionally charged.

TIMING MECHANISM

Capacitors can be used to delay or time a charge, for instance to control the energy stimulating a balance or tuning fork coil until the unit is in the proper position to receive that stimulus. If the capacitor is wired as simply as in Figure 116,

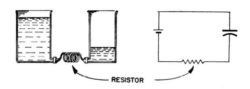

RESISTOR

FIGURE 121
A capacitor can be used to time a circuit by inserting a resistor to delay the charge from the battery, much as a thin tube impedes a flow of water from one tank to another.

the charge builds up in the unit almost immediately. However, including a resistor in the circuit impedes the flow of current. This is seen in Figure 121, analogous to a thin tube connecting two tanks of water. The long narrow passage of the tube delays the water, and the tanks take longer to equalize. Because of this same resistance, the capacitor takes longer to become charged to the same value as its "donor."

Previously, we discussed the capacitor and learned something about its characteristics—that it is essentially a reservoir for electricity, that it tends to equalize its source of voltage, and that it can be used, along with a resistor, to delay or time an electrical charge.

IN THE ACCUTRON

As we examine the Accutron circuit, we can learn more about the capacitor's action in a timepiece, as well as understand the Accutron better.

We know the Accutron operates on the vibrations of a tuning fork, rather than by the oscillations of a balance wheel and hairspring. The tines of the fork are equipped with magnetic cups at each tip. Mounted within each cup is a conical magnet, surrounded by insulated wire, which serve as *driving coils*. One of them functions also, as a *phase sensing coil*. Energy provided by a tiny battery sets up an electronic circuit between these coils and magnets, causing the tuning fork to vibrate continuously. To maintain this vibration, the coils must receive a pulse of current from the battery at just the exact instant. As the tuning fork vibrates, an alternating voltage is induced in the two coils. This voltage is a direct measure of the amplitude of the tuning fork's vibration. It is also this voltage which helps the circuit sense the timing and control the amplitude of vibration.

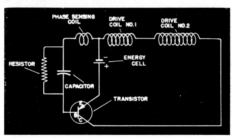

FIGURE 122: In the Accutron circuit, the capacitor, along with its resistor, keeps the transistor in a nonconducting state through most of the cycle operating the tuning fork.

As we notice in *Figure 122*, the capacitor lies parallel in the circuit to a resistor. This resistor causes a slight leak in the capacitor's charge; thus the capacitor will be recharged slightly at each peak of the alternating voltage induced in the phase sensing coil by the magnets. These pulses of current cause the transistor to conduct and let current flow into the driving coils to maintain vibrations of the tuning fork. Therefore, we see that the capacitor, with its resistor, is the element which keeps the transistor in a non-conducting state through most of the cycle operating the tuning fork. If the amplitude of the tuning fork's magnets is such that at the instant the transistor becomes conducting, the induced voltage in the drive coil equals the battery voltage, no current will flow, since the two voltages are opposite in polarity and would cancel each other.

The amplitude is controlled by maintaining the induced voltage in the drive coil at 10 per cent less than the battery voltage. The key to this is in the design of the magnet and coil system. In case of shock, a 10 per cent increase in amplitude of the tuning fork tines would cause the driving current pulses to be stopped and the tuning fork would then rapidly return to its proper amplitude. If the tuning fork should decrease its amplitude 10 per cent for any reason, the driving current would then be comparatively doubled, causing the tuning fork to pick up amplitude.

PRESERVING BATTERY LIFE

Another use of the capacitor in a timepiece circuit is to suppress a regenerative current, which would otherwise exhaust the battery. Such a circuit was shown in *Figure 107* and is repeated here.

While a capacitor is composed of one conducting metal separated from another conductor by an insulator, we may even call a coil a capacitor. Multiply a few adjacent turns of wire by the hundreds in a watch or clock coil, and we have a capacitor of noticeable size and electrical value. By placing one coil next to or even inside a similar coil, we have additional capacitance.

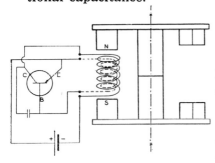

Current sent through a coil generates a magnetic field around it. When this current is stopped, the magnetic field collapses back into the coil in the opposite direction. In *Figure 123*, one coil is wound within the other; when current in the first collapses, it induces a current of opposite polarity in the second coil, which, being only momentary, quickly collapses also, inducing a current again in the first coil. This is repeated back and forth. It would eventually die out, but the initial surge of

FIGURE 123: A capacitor is inserted in this circuit to save the life of the battery as the relaxed backsurge of current through one coil induces a momentary current in the adjacent coil, constantly stimulating the battery to supply current to maintain the circuit.

alternating current has sufficient intensity to influence the transistor to conduct. This in turn would cause the battery to supply additional current to overcome the circuit's losses. The electrical oscillation would continue until the battery becomes exhausted. Thus the circuit would drain the battery without providing power to compensate.

To overcome this difficulty, a capacitor, shown in *Figure 123*, is placed in the circuit. It is charged and discharged by the alternating action just explained. As it discharges, the capacitor bucks the regenerative current, cancelling out the electric oscillation and conserving the battery's life so that it can supply pulses to the coil to stimulate the balance magnets at just the right instant.

TO PREVENT ARCING

Capacitors are used in some cases as spark suppressors. When a circuit using an iron core coil is broken, a spark would ordinarily jump across the contacts or switch points. If a capacitor is connected across these points, the electrical charge caused by the collapsing magnetic field will be used to charge the capacitor instead, preventing arcing.

DISCRIMINATING A CURRENT

Since capacitors allow the passage of AC current but block DC current, they can be used in circuits where the discrimination of one from another is important.

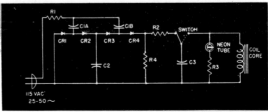

FIGURE 124: **Modern watch demagnetizer:** inside view. Watch is placed on top in a recess which aligns it with the demagnetizing coil of enamel wire wound on a powdered iron core. With the unit connected to AC current, the pushbutton is depressed. A neon lamp flashes to show the device is working. FIGURE 125: Scheme of demagnetizing unit: coil core is connected to the open switch. When not in use, the pushbutton's terminals complete a charging circuit to capacitor C3. When the button is depressed, the charging circuit is opened and the discharge circuit through the coil core is closed. As the capacitor's discharge current flows through the coil core, a ringing circuit composed of the coil core and C3 produces the damped AC wave which does the demagnetizing.

100

IN AN ELECTRONIC DEMAGNETIZER

Still another use of the capacitor is in the modern electronic demagnetizer. In this device, all electronic action takes place in about 1/20 of a second. Its purpose is to produce electronically and automatically that which old fashioned demagnetizers did by hand. By withdrawing a watch from the demagnetizer's coil, the magnetic influence of the alternating current on the watch gradually diminished. This produced a damped or diminishing wave of magnetic intensity and polarity.

Figure 124 shows the inside of this device with its iron core

DAMPED WAVE

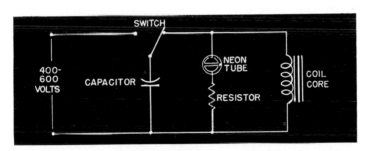

FIGURE 126: The damped wave, produced by a demagnetizer, dies down quickly from its maximum value to zero. FIGURE 127: The scheme of the electronic demagnetizer in Figure 125 is summarized more simply here.

coil. *Figure 125* shows its electronic scheme. From the regular 60 cycle AC source, the voltage is rectified and multiplied. The circuit to the left is closed and the capacitor is charged to approximately 600 volts.

When the watch is placed over the iron core coil and the switch turned to the right, the supplying circuit is opened but the right side of the circuit is closed. This allows the already charged capacitor to discharge through the iron core coil. A strong magnetic field forms around the coil and adjacent watch.

Notice that the energy which was stored in the capacitor as an electrostatic charge is now transferred to the coil as an electromagnetic field. When this magnetic field ends, it collapses suddenly, causing a back surge which recharges the capacitor in the opposite polarity. The capacitor is not as strongly recharged as originally, due to heat loss of energy in the coil windings. Because the circuit is still closed, the capacitor will discharge into the coil core again, more weakly. This repeats for several cycles until, like a freely swinging pendulum, it comes to rest, exhausted. Its wave grows weaker and weaker, like the damped sine wave shown in *Figure 126,* and the magnetism in the watch exhausted.

Figure 127 shows a simplified diagram of the right side of the Elimag's circuit. The switch to the right is closed. The capacitor discharges into the coil core. As the resistor is fed by the discharging capacitor, a small neon lamp flashes to indicate that the circuit is operating. As the magnetic field in the coil core collapses, it travels in reverse, creating a voltage of its own. We know that a capacitor tends to equalize the voltage of its source. In this case it will absorb the charge from the coil's collapsing magnetic field, and, since the coil is "vacant," the capacitor will "feed" the coil. This action oscillates back and forth until all of the energy is dissipated, producing the damped sine wave.

BATTERIES USED IN WATCHES

Watch	Model	Type Battery
Accutron	214	W-2 Special
Accutron	218	W-4 Special
Accutron	8DACD (ladies)	W-4 Special
Benrus	FU-3-13	WH-3
Beta 2	Quartz	WH-3
Beta 2	Quartz (thin cases)	WH-4
Caravelle	7 OT	Special (7.80x5.20mm)
Caravelle	12 OTC	301-U.C.
Citizen	X-8	301-U.C.
Citizen	1C-12(6x8)	WH-1
Elgin	725	W-1
Epperlein	100	NC-201
ESA	9150-9154-9162	WH-12, WH-12NM, Eveready 342 LeClanche MRNM
Girard-Perregaux	Quartz	Mallory, Mercury-Oxide
Hamilton	500	NC 201
Hamilton	505	S-41
Junghans	600 series	WH-3
Landeron	4750	WD-4
Landeron	4751	WD-5
Lip	R27	WD-2
Lip	FU-3	WH-3
Longines	Ultraquartz	WH-3
Lucien Picard		RM-312
Nepro	Electronic alarm	MS-13
PUW	1000-1001	Exp. 77 (U.C. 303)
Ruhla		WS-12
Seiko	3100 (balance wheel)	301-U.C.
Seiko	Quartz	303-U.C.
Thiel	25	WS-12
Timex	Type A Gents (Mercury)	WS-3
Timex	Type A Gents (Silver)	WS-12
Timex	Type B Ladies	WH-4
Unisonic	(Universal)	W-4 Special

Part 2
Electric Watch Repair

"ACCUTRON"
(BULOVA)

Bulova's "Accutron" like other tuning fork timepieces, is an electronic timepiece which eliminates not only the main-spring with its winding mechanism, and the escapement, but also does away with the balance and hairspring. At the heart of the principles which make "Accutron" possible is the tuning fork (Figure 2).

The Tuning Fork

The high accuracy of the fixed vibration frequency of tuning forks has long been known to students of physics. The rate at which these forks vibrate depends on the material of which they are made, their length, and the body.

If a tuning fork were electro-mechanically (or electronically) activated, engineers discovered, its vibrations could be made to push a wheel. Since the vibrations per second are fixed, steady and unchanging, each vibration would push the wheel at a most regular pace. Such a wheel could then be geared in a series with a train of wheels to move a set of hands.

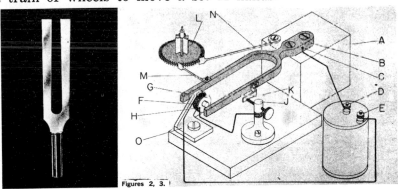

Figures 2, 3.

The Principle Explained

Figure 3 shows a simplified method by which a tuning fork can be made to vibrate continuously and move a gear. This should help prepare the reader for the more technical explanations of the electronic principle of "Accutron" which follow later on.

A is a block of wood upon which the entire unit is mounted. B is the magnetic tuning fork fastened to this step-block by two screws. C is a copper wire connected to the fork and terminating at the positive connection D of the battery (energy cell). At the negative connection E, is another wire which leads to F and is connected to a coil of copper wire G, wound around an iron core. This coil and its core are supported independently by the stand O, and no part of the coil or its core touches the tines of the fork. The other end of the coil of wire at H is connected to the stand J with its adjustable contact screw.

Connected to one of the tuning fork tines is a silver contact piece K, which the adjustable screw in J touches when the fork is at rest.

The circuit produces a flow of current from D to C through K, into the screw through the wire at H, and through the coil G, coming out at F, and then back to E. This causes the coil G to become an electro-magnet; and the coil's iron core attracts both tines of the ferro-magnetic tuning fork.

When the tines are attracted toward the iron core of the coil, the circuit is broken, because K loses contact with the adjustable screw in J. It is this loss of contact that interrupts the circuit; and the tines—because of their resiliency—return to their position of rest. But at the instant that it comes to rest, the tine at the right, through contact piece K, makes contact with adjustable screw J. This completes the circuit again, which causes the tines to move inward, towards the coil core, again breaking the circuit. Thus the vibration continues at its own musical pitch (fixed frequency) as long as the energy cell lasts.

The fork's other tine has attached near its end a thin spring M which engages at near tangency the ratchet-toothed wheel L. As the tine moves outward, the spring moves the wheel L one tooth. To prevent the ratchet wheel and pinion from turning backwards when the spring M and tine are attracted inward, lock spring N (attached to wood block A) is used. Spring N not only prevents backlash, but its slight side pressure against the slanted ratchet teeth positions the wheel for its next impulse by N. This action is similar to the draw in a jeweled lever escapement.

Difficulties Overcome

The preceding is an over-simplification. Such a device would have many drawbacks. One fault is that with each break of the contact between K and the adjustable screw at J, a spark would result. The spark would sap the energy from the battery and eventually cause the contacts to erode or carbonize. Furthermore, the amplitude of vibration of this type of tuning fork could increase, due to an increase in voltage or from a shock, and these wider vibrations would cause the pusher spring M to move wheel L more than one tooth at a time. Any horological mechanism attached to such a machine would gain time.

On the other hand, if the voltage dropped, the fork vibrations would become weaker. The amplitude would drop a bit, the tine which nudges wheel L would be too weak to advance the wheel, and the timepiece would stop.

Transistor's Function

In Bulova's "Accutron" these problems are eliminated. No sparking is possible because there is no physical contact or "break" to induce sparking. The release of energy from the power cell to the electro-magnetic coils is electronically accomplished through the use of a transistor. This does electronically what other devices do electro-mechanically. (The watch's general electronic system which does this will be described in detail.)

But here is a simplified explanation:

Figure 4 shows the actual tuning fork—the heart of "Accutron"—mounted on the movement plate. Attached to each of the tines of the fork is a magnetic iron cup, which faces outward. In the center of each cup is a thin, tapered permanent magnet. Mounted firmly on the movement case are two stationary hollow coils made of ultra- fine copper wire. They are connected to each other in series (Figure 5).

Figure 4. Tuning fork with magnetic iron cups is mounted on movement plate.

Figure 5. Spacing of magnetic cups at tip of fork around tiny electro-magnets is shown in this cross-section.

The transistor is in series with these coils and the combination is connected to a battery. The coils are precisely fixed so that there is ample clearance between the hollow part of each coil as it fits over the tapered magnet and the iron cup which fits over the coil. Therefore the tines with their outer cups and inner magnets can vibrate within and over the stationary coils without touching them. Figure 5 shows the right coil partially cut away to reveal its relationship to the cup and tine magnet.

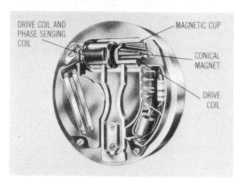

Figure 6. This is the basic mechanism of "Accutron." Tiny striped cylinder at 3 o'clock position is the resistor.

The Transistor-Switch

To follow the action, refer to Figure 6. It is necessary to imagine in ultra-slow motion action which actually takes place 360 times a second. When current flows through the coils, it attracts the tines. However, as we realize from our knowledge of electricity, when a permanent magnet moves through a coil of wire, it induces a current. Therefore, as the iron cup on each tine is attracted to the coil, its inner, permanent magnet moving through the coil induces a voltage. This induced voltage is in the reverse direction from the original voltage coming from the battery, and it cancels out the energizing voltage, causing the field partially to collapse. As the magnetic tines move back to their (original) point of rest, their attached magnets induce a voltage going in the opposite direction. A current travels through the transistor, which acts as a switch and which releases a new surge of current to again attract the tines. In other words, the transistor acts as a switch, allowing current from the battery to flow only when the voltage applied to it is sufficiently high A capacitor with a resistor across it is the element which maintains the transistor in a non-conducting condition through most of the cycle of operation of the tuning fork.

Figure 7 shows "Accutron" with the dial removed. Notice the fixed coils within the iron cups on the tines. The transistor is the cylindrical object near the 5 o'clock dial position. The striped cylindrical piece at the 3 o'clock position is the resistor. The toothed wheel enmeshed with the minute wheel is the hand setting wheel which is depressd into mesh with the minute wheel for the hand setting operation. This is done by a handle on the back of the watch case.

Figure 7. Enlargement of dial side of movement shows electronic circuit at right, tuning fork at center of photo.

Figure 8. Train-side view shows tiny mercury battery as circle at right, the tuning fork cups and coils at top.

Figure 8 shows the movement side of "Accutron." Here the magnetic cups can be seen. The mercury battery is the circular shape at the 3 o'clock position. The driving mechanism, similar to the system shown in Figure 3, is shown in Figure 9, also greatly simplified.

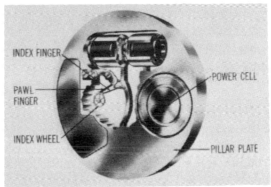

Figure 9. Diagram shows how the tuning fork's indexing finger whirls the index wheel at the rate of 360 teeth per second.

In "Accutron," the fork vibrates 360 times a second. There is no tick, but if the watch is held closely to the ear, a musical hum is heard. The physical pitch of middle C is 256 vibrations a second. The nearest tone to the watch's hum is F sharp (365.8 vibrations a second). Each of the vibrations is made to move a ratchet-toothed wheel by the width of one tooth. The wheel contains 300 teeth. Thus in one second, the tuning fork advances this gear one and a fifth turns. Geared to other train wheels, the speed is reduced to drive a full set of hands. The sweep second hand moves in an apparent continuous motion similar to that of an AC synchronous electric clock.

In an elementary example of the electro-magnetically activated

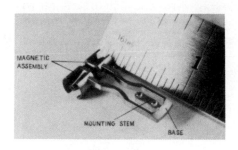

ACCUTRON Tuning Fork

tuning fork (Figure 3), we also showed that if the voltage increased, the tuning fork tines might vibrate with greater amplitude, and push the wheel a distance of more than one tooth. That would cause any timepiece connected to the mechanism to gain. Conversely, if the voltage dropped, the amplitude might be insufficient to advance the index wheel even one tooth.

Furthermore, a shock might increase or decrease the amplitude, causing erratic timekeeping. However, in Bulova's "Accutron," the problem has been solved in two ways. First, by the design of the ratchet toothed index wheel and its index and pawl jewels; this arrangement allows reasonable variations of amplitude—and yet the tine indexes only one tooth at a time. Second, by the electronic design (the transistor-electro-magnetic coils, phase-sensing coils, capacitor and resistor arrangement). This design will be explained in detail later in this chapter.

Amplitude Variance

While it might seem advantageous to keep the tines' amplitude to exact limits, this would not be advisable. If the voltage dropped, a diminishing of the amplitude would cause a failure of the index jewel to advance the one tooth required. On the other hand, should the voltage rise, or the watch receive a shock, the amplitude would increase, causing the index jewel to register more than one tooth. The increase would result in the timepiece's gaining time.

The index wheel contains 300 fine ratchet teeth. The diameter of this wheel is .095 inch, or 2.40mm. In familiar fractional inches, it is closest to 3/32-inch. This means that each tooth is .001 inch (.025mm); in other words, there is 1/1000 of an inch between the tips of each tooth. If I were required to make an accurate drawing of this precise and important index wheel so that each tooth would be ½ inch from tip to tip, I would have to draw the wheel four feet in diameter! If a 12-tooth sector of such a large wheel were then to be shown, the arc of such a wheel would appear nearly straight. Therefore, it will be simpler to show the indexing action with a series of enlarged teeth and index and pawl jewels on a straight line. (See Figure 11.)

Purposes of Pawl Jewel

The pawl jewel on the left is attached to the spring which in turn is attached to the plate. Its chief purpose is to prevent the index wheel from turning backward when the indexing jewel moves back in the return direction. Its second purpose is to draw the wheel backwards by the coincidence of its angle and pressure upon the inclined surface of the teeth. This works much in the manner of draw in a conventional lever escapement, keeping the fork against the banking pin.

The index jewel (attached to a finger-spring which is attached to the left tine of the tuning fork) moves the index wheel counterclockwise. The pawl jewel and index jewel are in a position of rest in the first sequence (panel A) in Figure 11. Notice that

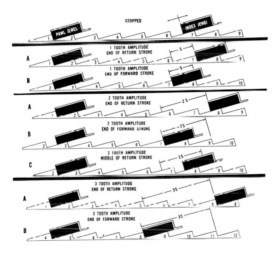

Figure 11. Diagram shows possible variations in index finger's 'push' regulated so ratchet toothed wheel always moves forward only one tooth's width.

the pawl jewel is resting snug against the edge of tooth 1 and flat against the surface of tooth 2. However, the index and pawl are positioned about half a tooth apart, so that at rest one or the other (or both) will exert the "draw effect" in the direction opposite from the normal movement.

When the tines are electro-magnetically activated and the jewel moves to the right on the return stroke (Sequence B), it moves just far enough to drop onto the front of tooth 7. There it rests on the incline of tooth 8. In sequence C the forward stroke (of a one-tooth amplitude), will advance tooth 7 one full position. The pawl jewel will lock tooth 2 and prevent backlash.

When the tine amplitude has caused the indexing jewel to move the equal of a two tooth movement (as shown in Sequence D, 2S), only one tooth of the index wheel will be advanced. Here the width of the return stroke of the index jewel's motion is equal to two teeth. It moves forward one half of this distance and because of the "draw" pressure of the index and pawl springs, the index wheel moves backward to the position midway between teeth 7 and 8.

On the forward stroke of the index finger and jewel with an amplitude equal to a width of two teeth (Sequence E), the index jewel has gathered up tooth 7 (see also Sequence D) and moved it to a point one-half tooth width beyond its position of rest. Notice that tooth 2 is one-half tooth width beyond the pawl jewel.

When the indexing thrust of the indexing finger and jewel are returning as in Sequence F, the torque (draw-pressure) of both pawl and index jewels and fingers on the inclined surface of the index wheel teeth will cause that wheel to recoil slightly until a tooth such as Number 2 in F, C, and A rests against the front edge of the pawl jewel.

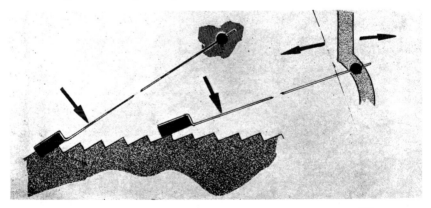

Figure 12

Figure 12 shows how this "draw" angle operates. Imagine the springs which contain the epoxy-bonded pawl and index jewels exerting a slight pressure in a near radial direction. This would cause a recoil of the ratchet tooth. It is this allowable recoil which permits the tines to move the index wheel a distance equal to a limit of almost three teeth amplitude, and yet register only a one-tooth advance. This gives a wide tolerance in the tuning fork amplitude with no gain or loss of time.

However, should the amplitude of the tuning fork exceed these limits, for instance, equal to an amplitude of slightly over three teeth, then the arrangement just explained would be inoperative —and all three teeth would be gathered up. This is shown in Sequences G and H, Figure 11. Here the return stroke of the index jewel starts from a point of rest against tooth 5 and ends three teeth back in front of tooth 8. Notice that the same amplitude on the forward stroke would actually gather up the three teeth which will be "counted" by the dial train. This is shown at the left, at which point teeth 2, 3, and 4 have been gathered and retained.

Despite its small size, the physical principle and action of the index wheel and pawl and index jewel and springs are the same whether the wheel is 1/10th of an inch or 4 feet in diameter.

Amplitude Control, Electronically

To safeguard against such extremes of amplitude in which more than one tooth would be counted with each vibration of the tuning fork, "Accutron" has provided a unique amplitude control system designed into the electronic circuit driving the tuning fork.

Interrelationship of the Electro-Magnetic Elements

Before discussing the electronic circuit in "Accutron," let us examine the interrelationship of the magnetic elements on the tuning fork tines and the coils of wire connected to the electronic circuit. The cup-like part attached to each tuning fork tine

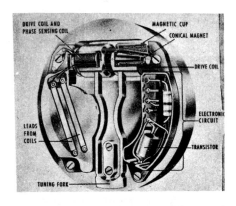

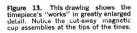
Figure 13. This drawing shows the timepiece's "works" in greatly enlarged detail. Notice the cut-away magnetic cup assemblies at the tips of the tines.

(Figure 13) is made of iron as it must be magnetic. Mounted in the center of each of these cups is a conical magnet. Between the cup and its central magnet is a strong magnetic field. The coils of wire wound on the plastic forms extend into the space between the respective magnets and cups and these coils therefore lie within the magnetic field without touching the moving parts attached to the tuning fork. These coils are supported by the pillar plate.

If a current is passed through one of these coils of wire, this coil becomes an electro-magnet. It will then either attract or repel the associated magnet and cup assembly, depending upon the polarity of the voltage applied. Conversely, if a magnet and cup assembly is moved within its associated coil, a voltage is induced in this coil. The polarity of this voltage depends upon which direction the magnet assembly is moved. This means that as the tuning fork vibrates, an alternating voltage is induced in the coils. This induced voltage is a direct measure of the amplitude of the tuning fork. It is this voltage which permits the circuit to sense and control the amplitude of vibration.

Dual-Purpose Coil

One other feature of the arrangement of the electro-magnetic parts which can be observed on this photograph (Figure 13) is that there are four wires leading from the coil on the left. This coil is in two sections with one end of each section connected together. The result is that while most of the turns of wire on the left hand coil are used to drive the tuning fork, approximately one quarter are used to form what is termed the "phase sensing coil." It is this coil which initiates the pulses of current into the driving coils at the proper instant to maintain the oscillations of the tuning fork.

The coils and associated magnets shown in this figure therefore serve three functions: first, they convert pulses of electrical current into mechanical impulses which drive the tuning fork; second, they provide the means by which the electronic circuit may sense the tuning fork amplitude; third, they control the instant in the tuning fork cycle during which the driving current pulse is delivered.

Operation of the Electronic Circuit

In the "Accutron," the tuning fork is impulsed electro-magnetically once each cycle. To avoid sparking as in electric watches, the impulsing is accomplished by an electronic circuit. Hence the problems of make and break contacts are avoided. The activation of the electric watches' mechanically operated switch is accomplished in "Accutron" in a trouble-free manner by the phase sensing coil which causes the current in the tuning fork driving coils to be turned on and off. *The transistor is the electronic element which turns the current on and off under the control of the phase sensing coil.* The transistor in "Accutron" therefore functions as a switch.

The transistor in "Accutron" has three leads: the emitter, base, and collector respectively. The base to emitter leads must be supplied with a current in order to cause the emitter to collector circuit to be conducting. In other words, the collector circuit can conduct only when there is current in the base circuit of the transistor.

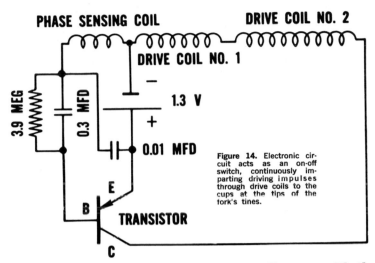

Figure 14. Electronic circuit acts as an on-off switch, continuously imparting driving impulses through drive coils to the cups at the tips of the fork's tines.

Figure 14 shows the schematic wiring diagram with the electrical connections between the various circuit elements. To repeat, the transistor functions as a switch, which can be caused to conduct or to be non-conducting. The *left hand side of this diagram* contains all the elements for turning the driving current on and off. First, let us examine the manner in which this occurs.

The *capacitor,* shown on the left with a *resistor* across it, is the element which maintains the transistor in a non-conducting condition through most of the cycle of operation of the tuning fork. As explained previously, an alternating voltage is induced in the phase sensing coil by the vibrations of the magnet associated with it. In combination with the emitter to base circuit of the transistor, which acts as a diode or rectifier, this voltage is added to the power cell voltage to charge the capacitor. A capacitor functions as a storage tank for electricity. The resistor across the "Accutron" capacitor causes a slight leak with the result that this capacitor will be re-charged slightly once each cycle by the peaks of the alternating voltage induced in the phase sensing coil. It is these recharging pulses of current which allow the transistor to conduct momentarily and cause current to flow in the driving coils to pulse the tuning fork and maintain its vibrations.

The right hand side of this diagram contains all the elements for delivering pulses of current to the tuning fork drive coils and for controlling the size of these current pulses so that proper tuning fork amplitude is maintained. The drive coils are connected in series with the power cell and the emitter-to-collector-circuit to the transistor. The emiter-to-collector-circuit is caused to conduct at the instant when the voltage induced in the drive coils is about at its maximum instantaneous value and is opposite in polarity to power cell voltage. Therefore, if the amplitude of the tuning fork should be such that at the instant the transistor becomes conducting the induced voltage in the drive coils exactly equals the power cell voltage, no current would flow since there would be no net voltage because the drive coil induced voltage "bucks" the power cell voltage.

The magnet and coil system is so designed that at the proper amplitude of vibration for the tuning fork, the voltage induced in the drive coils has a peak value about 10 per cent less than power cell voltage. This is the key to the operation of the amplitude control system. Because of this a 10 per cent increase in amplitude, resulting from a disturbance, would cause the driving current pulses to be reduced to zero and the tuning fork would rapidly return to its proper amplitude. Furthermore, a 10 per cent decrease in the amplitude of the tuning fork would cause the driving current pulses to double and again return the tuning fork very rapidly to the proper amplitude.

In principle, it has been shown that the tuning fork amplitude is controlled by converting it into a voltage, which is maintained at a value about 10 per cent below power cell voltage. This cell is designed to provide a very constant voltage for approximately 99 per cent of its useful life, hence the tuning fork amplitude remains at its proper value. If the amplitude changes due to a shock, it will return to the proper value within a very small fraction of a second because of the amplitude control circuit just described.

REGULATING the Accutron is done by changing the frequency of the tuning fork. As mentioned earlier, this frequency depends upon the effective length of the tuning fork as well as its mass and the material from which it was made. The effective length of the fork can be altered by shifting the center of gravity of the tines. If the center of gravity is moved outward, away from its center, the frequency of vibration will be less and the Accutron will lose time. If the center of gravity is moved closer to the center of the tuning fork, the frequency will increase and the Accutron will gain time.

Such changes are accomplished by the pronged, frictioned, spring-clip which is attached to each of the cups at the tips of the tuning fork tines (Figure 15). These clips are the regulators.

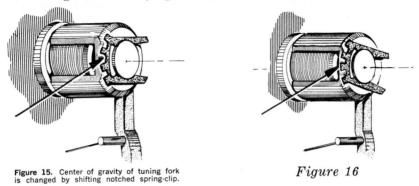

Figure 15. Center of gravity of tuning fork is changed by shifting notched spring-clip.

Figure 16

The prongs of these regulator-clips are called "lands" and the notches between them are termed "grooves."

By twisting the clip so that a land occupies the spot formerly occupied by the adjacent groove, a change of two seconds a day can be obtained.

In Figure 16, the regulator has been twisted one "land" in the clockwise direction. This has caused a very slightly heavier mass to be positioned upwards of the tine, causing an outward shift in the center of gravity. As a result, the watch will show a time loss of exactly two seconds daily.

However, a correction as small as ½ second a day can be made by moving the regulator only one-quarter of a division. There are seven divisions on each of the regulators (4 lands, 3 grooves). Thus, because each division is equal to 2 seconds per day, it would be impossible to make a correction of more than 28 seconds per day, even if both regulators were originally set all the way in or out (which they are not). An Accutron which gains or loses more than about a minute a week requires *servicing*—not regulation. Altitude affects it at the rate of one second+ for every 1500 feet.

Setting the Hands

Unlike ordinary, mainspring-powered watches, this electronic watch does not have a stem or crown on the side of the case. The setting crown has been placed on the back of the Accutron so that no projection interrupts the smooth contour of the case. Its

115

location is shown in Figure 17. By lifting the setting handle to an upright position, as in Figure 18, the setting mechanism is engaged. This is equivalent to pulling out the crown on an ordinary watch. The hands can then be set by rotating the setting handle either clockwise or counter-clockwise to bring the hands to the desired position. The handle (or latch as it may be called) is then folded down. This is the same as pressing in the crown of an ordinary watch after setting. These stems are available in eight overall lengths to allow complete return to the neutral position.

Lifting the Setting Handle   *Figure 17*   Setting the Hands   *Figure 18*

Changing the Power Cell

Figure 19 shows how the power cell (battery) is removed for replacement. The hatch opposite the setting crown is grooved to accommodate a coin, which may be used to unscrew the hatch.

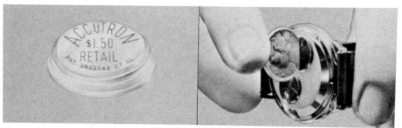

The ACCUTRON Power Cell   *Figure 19*

In Figure 19, a dime has been used to open the gasketed hatch. Turning the watch to dial-up position will now cause the old power cell to drop out. A new power cell can then be tucked into the empty compartment, after which the hatch is screwed down tightly to assure that the watch will be waterproof.

Position Errors

The position error of the Accutron is very small. All Accutrons have the same relative performance in the same position.

116

Wrist watches are generally tested in the dial up, dial down, 3 down, 12 down and 9 down position. The maximum difference in any of these positions in *all* Accutrons is *always* 5 seconds per day. Unlike balance-wheeled watches, this positional error is a function of design and cannot be altered or "adjusted" by the watchmaker. It is a small but predictable error.

The effect of various positions on the rate of this electronic

Figures 20, 21, 22. Tuning fork at left (horizontal) has no position error; down position (center) causes five seconds per day increase; and fork in up position at right slows watch five seconds per day.

watch can best be explained by referring again to the classical tuning fork. When the long dimension of the tuning fork is horizontal as shown in Figure 20, the frequency of vibration does not vary whether the tines of the fork are along side of each other or one over the other. This is because gravity has no effect on a horizontal tuning fork. In most models of this watch, the tuning fork is mounted along the 12-6 axis of the movement. The rates in dial-up, dial-down, 3-down and 9-down positions will therefore be precisely the same.

When the long dimension of the tuning fork is vertical with the tines down (Figure 21), which is the 12-down position in most models of this watch, the effect of gravity causes a slightly higher tuning fork frequency. In this position, the watch's rate is 5 seconds per day faster than when the fork is in the horizontal position.

Conversely, as shown in Figure 22, when the fork is vertical with the tines up (the 6-down position in most models of the Accutron), the frequency of the fork will decrease, causing a rate 5 seconds per day slower than when the fork is in the horizontal position. The 6-down position is rarely experienced when this watch is worn on the outside of the wrist.

This small position error is taken into consideration in the regulation of the watch at the factory. It is regulated for perfect timekeeping when worn on the outer side of the wrist. It is recommended that if the owner prefers to wear this watch on the inner side of his wrist (making the 6-down position occur more frequently) the watch should be regulated 3 seconds per day faster than the original factor adjustment.

Temperature Effects

The effect of various temperatures on the rate of the Accutron is far less than on conventional wrist watches. Accutron is designed for accurate performance under temperature extremes from 20° to 120° F. Outside this range, it may not keep time accurately, but this is of small concern since wrist watches are usually only a few degrees apart from body temperature, even in extreme cold or hot weather.

Power Cell

The power cell used in this electronic watch is a special mercury unit which operates at about 1.3 volts. It is designed to supply power at its rated voltage for at least a year. Although it seems to be the same sort of cell which is used in hearing aids, the necessity of maintaining level output for a long period at an extremely low current drain (less than 1 per cent of that used in a hearing aid) required a special design.

According to information from Bulova, if a hearing-aid battery were used in this watch, it would fail after a few months' operation and serious damage to the movement may result from cell leakage. Only the genuine Bulova Accutron power cell is recommended by them for use in this watch. It is suggested that the customer change the power cell every 12 months, perhaps on his birthday or some other significant anniversary, or on the date he received the watch.

Resistance to Shock

The most delicate parts of most watches are the balance pivots and jewels. Some of these have shock resistant devices. In Bulova's electronic tuning fork watch, shock protection has been provided by the use of a shock *bridge* and *stops* to limit the movement of the tuning fork tines so that they cannot be deformed by severe jolting. A guard surrounding the index and jewel fingers has also been provided.

Anti-Magnetic Properties

The criterion for an "anti-magnetic" watch is as follows: When subjected to a magnetic field with a strength of 60 Gauss and then removed from this influence, the watch shall operate without being affected more than 15 seconds per day. Since it has neither balance wheel nor hairspring, the Accutron avoids much of this fault, changing rate only a few seconds per day.

The watch should not be deliberately exposed to a powerful magnetic field such as a demagnetizer or a strong permanent magnet, since this could demagnetize the permanent magnets on each of the tuning fork tines. However, in normal use, this watch can be considered "anti-magnetic." Should the Accutron be accidentally demagnetized, the tuning fork must be returned to Bulova for re-magnetizing.

Servicing

Figure 23 shows the units of a disassembled Accutron movement. Compared to the mainspring-driven watch, there are relatively few parts. Because of the absence of high torque as in mainspring watches, deterioration of oil and parts will not occur

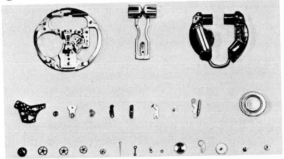

Figure 23. When compared with mainspring-driven watches, "Accutron" movement has relatively few parts.

as rapidly. Therefore, Bulova claims that the Accutron does not require frequent periodic cleaning for reasons of preventive maintenance.

Replacement of parts is done on the module system such as is employed by the Armed Forces. A module is a unit which can be replaced easily and simply without need for repair or adjustment. The Accutron contains two sub-assemblies or modules, which can be removed and replaced as separate units, and which do not lend themselves to "field repair." These are the complete coil assembly, consisting of the entire electronic circuit and all electrical connections; and the complete fork assembly consisting of the tuning fork, magnets and magnetic cups, the index finger and jewel. The other parts of the Accutron will be familiar to all watchmakers.

The amplitude of the tuning fork is not affected by sound waves originating outside the watch.

Shocks do not cause the index and pawl jewels to "overbank" or jump on the side of the wheel. This is because the jewels, which straddle the thin index wheels are rather wide; these jewels also serve as banking guards for the index finger jewel.

WHEN THE ACCUTRON malfunctions, the trouble will probably lie in two main divisions—the indexing mechanism and train of gears, or in the electronic circuit with its electro-magnetic unit and tuning fork.

Since proper diagnosis is so important before the watchmaker begins his work, Bulova recommends the following kit. It consists of a microscope which has proper features for examining the indexing mechanism; a special test set for checking power cell voltage and electronic circuit operation, and to provide a special voltage for checking and adjusting the indexing mechanism; a special holder-jig which gives maximum protection to the movement during servicing and adjustment; an index finger post wrench; and a waterproof case wrench.

Microscope Needed

The most critical test in the diagnosis of Accutron malfunctions is the check on the indexing mechanism, mentioned so often before. The index wheel is not only small (just under 1/10th of an inch), but it contains 300 teeth which are only 1/1000th inch

Figure 24

apart. The jewels of the index and pawl fingers are only 7/1000th of an inch square and only 1/500th of an inch thick. These dimensions are too fine to be seen objectively with the naked eye, or even with the most powerful bench loupe. Therefore, it will be necessary to use a microscope to magnify the unit sufficiently to check its function. (After checking the indexing mechanism, the actual adjustment can be made with a loupe if preferred.) Any microscope can be used if it has these qualifications: 20 to 30 diameters magnification, a wide field upright image, and approximately two-inch working distance. Generally, biological and metallurgical microscopes are unsuited for watch repair because they have a small field, short focal length and working distance, and give an inverted image. A recommended type of microscope is shown in Figure 24.

A second piece of equipment needed is shown in Figure 25. It has three important functions. First, it is used as a voltmeter to check power cell voltage. Second, it can be used to check the current that is drawn by the electronic circuit and indicate its operating condition. Third, it is used to supply smaller amounts of power for the adjustment of the indexing mechanism.

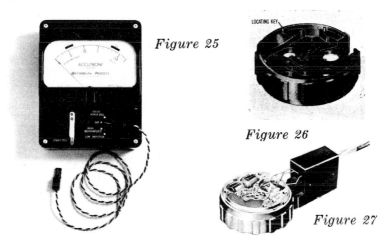

Figure 25

Figure 26

Figure 27

A movement holder with special molded surfaces on the bottom and top is an essential specialized piece of equipment for use with the Accutron. For example, it prevents damage to the indexing mechanism and permits removal of the tuning fork and coil circuit assembly. This holder *must* be used in removing the coil and fork to prevent damage to the delicate mechanism. One side of the holder contains a "nest" which receives the coil and fork assembly. The holder has a locating key (Figure 26) so the movement is accurately positioned. This holder is also a *"must"* when checking and adjusting the important indexing mechanism. The notch in the side of the holder is designed to permit the spring clip (Figure 27) of the test set to be attached to the movement.

121

TROUBLE SHOOTING CHART

PROBLEM	POSSIBLE CAUSES (in order of probability)	DIAGNOSIS PROCEDURE	REMEDIAL ACTION
GAINING OR LOSING A FEW SECONDS A DAY	Abnormal wearing habits or Improper regulation		Regulate
STOPPED (No hum)	1. Exhausted Power Cell	Check Power Cell voltage. If low or no voltage, Power Cell is exhausted.	Replace Power Cell
	2. Faulty electronic circuit	If voltage is normal, check current. If no current, electronic circuit is faulty	Replace complete coil assembly (Part No. 711)
	3. Mechanical blockage of tuning fork	If current is high, check if tuning fork is blocked	Find blockage and remove it
	4. Faulty electronic circuit	If no blockage of tuning fork, electronic circuit is faulty	Replace complete coil assembly (Part No. 711)
STOPPED (Sweep second hand does not turn but fork hums)	1. Exhausted Power Cell	Check Power Cell voltage. If voltage is low, Power Cell is exhausted	Replace Power Cell
	2. Indexing mechanism maladjustment	If voltage normal, open case, remove movement, expose indexing mechanism, and examine under microscope. Check index jewel engagement	Readjust indexing mechanism if necessary
	3. Mechanical blockage of train	If jewels appear normal, check train freedom. Train may be blocked	Find mechanical blockage and remove it
	4. Dirt on index wheel	If train is free, and index jewel engagement is correct, tap movement lightly with pencil to increase fork amplitude, while observing closely with loupe. If index wheel rotates once and then stops again, this is evidence of dirt on index wheel tooth	Clean entire movement in ultrasonic cleaner
	5. Damaged teeth on index wheel	If symptoms persist after cleaning, index wheel has been damaged	Change index wheel
GAINING OR LOSING EXCESSIVELY	1. Tuning fork not free	Open case, remove movement and check current. If current too high, examine for obvious foreign material interfering with free vibrations of tuning fork	If foreign matter is observed, remove same and recheck to see that current is normal
	2. Defective coil	If current too high and no evidence tuning fork is not free, expose indexing mechanism, disengage pawl jewel and check current again. If current remains high, coil assembly is defective	Replace complete coil assembly (Part No. 711)
	3. Mechanical interference in train	If current drops within "OK" range or below in 2, above, cause is excessive train friction	Find interference and remove it
	4. Foreign material clinging to magnetic elements	If current is "OK" in 1, above, and rate is many seconds per day slow, check for loose screw or other matter clinging to a tuning fork magnet	Find foreign matter and remove same
	5. Indexing mechanism maladjustment	If current is "OK" in 1, above, indexing mechanism may be out of adjustment	Check and readjust indexing mechanism as necessary
	6. Dirt in index wheel teeth	If current and indexing mechanism adjustment have been found correct, there may be dirt in index wheel teeth	Clean entire movement

A regular waterproof wrench to fit the case back is also part of the kit. The kit is completed with the addition of a special wrench (shown in Figure 28), an aligning tool. Its tip is hollow

Figure 28

and is designed to align the index jewel finger. In use, it is placed over the end of the finger post on the tuning fork tine and gently stressed in the direction which will align the index jewel properly.

Diagnosis

With the exception of a broken crystal or loose hands, the possible causes for complaints on this watch will be:
  (1) It loses or gains a few seconds a day;
  (2) It gains or loses more than a minute a week;
  (3) It has stopped.

Unlike ordinary balance wheel watches that can have large timing errors regulated out, the Accutron has no wearing conditions or environmental effects to affect timing more than a few seconds a day. If the Accutron has stopped, be sure to listen carefully for the characteristic hum. If you can hear it, the fork is vibrating. Perhaps, then, the trouble is in the mechanical system—possibly in the indexing unit or the gear train.

On the other hand, if the watch is silent there may be some malfunction in the power cell, electronic circuit or tuning fork. Like all diagnoses (or in murder mystery stories), the process of finding the "guilty party" is to eliminate suspects and narrow the field down to one "culprit." So it is with this watch. The trouble-shooting chart on the opposite page is submitted here to acquaint the watchmaker with all possible malfunctions.

The post on the tuning fork, its projecting spring-finger and jewel assembly, as well as the spring-finger and pawl jewel, are very delicate. Therefore, when removing the hands, be careful neither to let the train spin forward nor force it backward—this will damage the indexing mechanism. Avoid unnecessary handling, but when it is absolutely necessary to handle them, be cautious. If it is necessary to handle the indexing wheel   be especially careful in removing it.   To avoid damaging the very fine teeth, never grasp the wheel with tweezers. Instead, handle the wheel by grasping the pinion.

In removing the coil assembly do not scratch or pierce the insulation on the wires or coils.

Do not demagnetize an Accutron or subject it to any high strength magnetic fields. Since this watch is based on electromagnetism, anything affecting the permanent magnets on the tuning fork will also seriously affect the operation of the timepiece.

Keep anything made of steel away from the tines of the tuning fork. The tine magnets are very powerful and will attract themselves to larger steel articles. Even the smallest magnetic particls may damage the fork or affect the timing.

Do not oil the teeth of the index wheel or the pawl or index jewels.

Do not bend the tines of the tuning fork. It will so seriously affect its timekeeping ability that it will have to be replaced.

Testing

Here's how to test the Accutron:

Before any other work is done, check the Power Cell to make sure that it is functioning properly.

1. Wipe the back of the case to remove any loose material near the Cell cover (to prevent the entrance of dirt when the cover is removed).

2. Unscrew the Cell compartment cover using a U.S. dime.

3. Turn the timepiece over and the Cell will fall out.

4. Place the Power Cell in the nest of the Test Set with the smaller diameter *down*.

5. Turn the rotary switch to "CHECK POWER CELL" position.

6. Read the Power Cell Voltage on the right-hand scale. The voltage reading should be in the "OK" area of the scale (1.25 to 1.45 volts). If it is, the Power Cell is in satisfactory operating condition.

Note: Poor electrical contact between Power Cell and Test Set will cause either a low reading or a wavering indication of cell voltage. It can be readily avoided by making certain that Cell surfaces and contacting points of the Test Set nest and clip are clean. Rubbing or twisting a suspected cell between the contacts while checking voltage is good practice. A wavering reading of voltage is *always* an indication of poor contact, not an indication of a bad cell. Testing should always be done with the authorized ACCUTRON Test Set or with any other equivalent high-resistance voltmeter with not less than 10,000 ohms per volt sensitivity. (A low-resistance voltmeter is not suitable.)

To check the electronic circuit, remove the movement from its case. Place the movement in its movement holder dial side down with the power cell recess adjacent to the notch in the side of the holder. With the power cell still in the test set clip, connect the spring clip at the end of the lead to the movement so the center finger touches the contact in the center of the power cell recess. This connects the power cell to the movement through the meter. The meter will give a reading of current on the left-hand scale.

Sometimes it may be necessary to tap the movement slightly to start the tuning fork vibrating after connecting the clip. The current reading should be in the "O.K." area of the scale (4.5 to 7.0 microamperes). If the movement be warmer than average room temperature (from nearness to a lamp bulb or being held in the hand) it may cause a reading higher than the "O.K." area. Let the movement cool to room temperature for a half hour and recheck it.

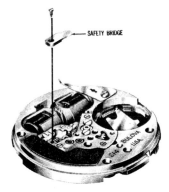

SAFETY BRIDGE

Figure 29

The purpose of checking and adjusting the indexing mechanism is to control the alignment, depth of engagement, and distance between the index and pawl jewels. Figure 29 shows how to expose the index mechanism. First, remove the safety bridge screw. Loosen the index guard screw as shown in Figure 30 and turn the index guard away from the wheel (guard should only be turned out of the way—not removed). Be careful not to hurt the index or pawl fingers which run through the guard (see Figure 35). Loosen the pawl bridge locking screw slightly, but leave the pawl adjusting bridge screw tight as shown in Figure 30. Observe the movement under the microscope to make certain that the pawl is engaged with the index wheel. The pawl must be engaged with the index wheel so the latter will remain stationary during the check for engagement. If it is engaged, rotate the pawl bridge cam until the pawl is brought into contact with the wheel.

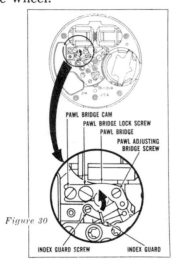

PAWL BRIDGE CAM
PAWL BRIDGE LOCK SCREW
PAWL BRIDGE
PAWL ADJUSTING BRIDGE SCREW

Figure 30

INDEX GUARD SCREW   INDEX GUARD

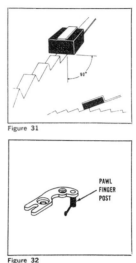

Figure 31

PAWL FINGER POST

Figure 32

Under the microscope, check both jewels to be sure the fingers are straight. Also ascertain that the jewels are centered on the wheel and perpendicular to the wheel as shown in Figure 31. If they are off-center, straighten them with the index finger post wrench. Place the wrench over the post on the tuning fork tine. Stress it gently to center the jewel on the wheel. The pawl jewel can be centered by bending its finger post (see Figure 32) with tweezers. If either jewel is not perpendicular to the plane of the wheel, correct it by lightly twisting the jewel finger close to the point when it is pinned (don't touch the jewel itself).

Here's how to check the engagement of the index jewel: Grasp the tine at the cup, preferably with tweezers made of non-magnetic alloy. Count the number of teeth before the index jewel pulls away from the wheel. The jewel should remain engaged with the wheel for five to seven teeth. If the number is less than five or greater than seven, modify it near the end where it is pinned by *gently* pressing the index finger toward or away from the wheel. Use the end of the tweezers or a needle as you would bend a hairspring near its stud. Check the engagement after each adjustment for the proper engagement. (See Figure 33).

126

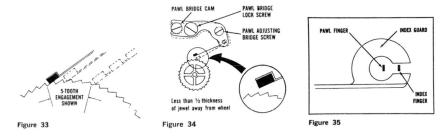

PAWL BRIDGE CAM   PAWL BRIDGE
                   LOCK SCREW

                   PAWL ADJUSTING
                   BRIDGE SCREW

5-TOOTH
ENGAGEMENT
SHOWN

Less than ½ thickness
of jewel away from wheel

PAWL FINGER   INDEX GUARD

INDEX
FINGER

Figure 33   Figure 34   Figure 35

Next, using a loupe, completely disengage the pawl jewel by rotating the pawl bridge adjusting cam until the bridge is at its maximum distance from the index wheel (Figure 34). Then examine the pawl jewel under the microscope. It should not touch the index wheel; it should be separated from the latter by a distance less than half the thickness of the jewel. You can adjust this distance by pressing gently in or out on the pawl finger, as described earlier.

With the power cell still in the test set clip, turn the right hand switch to the "Low Amplitude" position and turn the meter control switch to "Read Microamperes." Using the spring clip, attach the test set to the movement. The notch provided in the movement holder will cause contact between the spring clip, power cell and movement. The tuning fork should then begin to vibrate; but if it doesn't, an excess current reading will show on the meter. Tap the movement lightly and the tuning fork will begin to vibrate, decreasing the current reading to the lower end of the "O.K." area or slightly below it.

To bring the pawl toward the wheel, rotate the cam slowly in either direction until the watch begins to run. You can observe this without the microscope by watching the visible wheels. Next, turn the cam further in the same direction until the watch stops; then continue still further until the watch starts again and continues to run. At this point the adjustment is complete.

Tighten the pawl bridge lock screw and pawl adjusting bridge screw to prevent the bridge from moving out of its position. The watch should continue to run. If it doesn't the adjustment just explained must be repeated. Then disconnect the test set spring clip from the movement. Loosen the index guard screw and turn the index guard back into position, the index finger should pass through a point slightly inside the center of the slot in the guard (Figure 35). The index finger should not touch either side of the slot. If it does, lightly bend the guard to center the index finger, making certain that the pawl finger does not touch the guard. Finally, replace the safety bridge and safety bridge screw.

As a last check on the adjustment, time the watch accurately for at least an hour. If it is off more than a second, the trouble may be dirt on the index wheel or an incorrect adjustment of the indexing procedure. Check the index wheel under the microscope for dirt or damage.

If the trouble-shooting chart indicates some fault in the gear train, check the train's freedom by moving one of the wheels with tweezers. (This is not altogether recommended because it might damage the index and pawl fingers and jewels unless the wheels are rotated in the correct direction.) The simplest, safest and most convenient method to test the freedom of the train is to pluck the tuning fork tine to which the index finger is attached. The tine will vibrate a few seconds and the motion should cause the index wheel and the rest of the gear train to move. Even if the tine vibrated for only a second, it would be long enough to watch the index wheel make more than a full revolution. You can watch the process either with a loupe or the microscope. If you have checked the indexing mechanism and now pluck the tuning fork without producing motion in the train, you may conclude that the train is blocked.

METHODS OF ASSEMBLY AND DISASSEMBLY

Removing Hand, Dial and Dial Train

Disassembly

1. Remove the ground strap so movement can be placed in holder.
2. Remove the two dial holding nuts. Exact location is shown in Figure 36.
3. Use hand remover to remove hands.
4. Remove the dial. (Figure 37)
5. Remove the hour wheel.
6. Remove the cannon pinion.
7. Remove the setting wheel spring and minute wheel spring which are held by one setting wheel spring screw.
8. Remove the minute wheel.

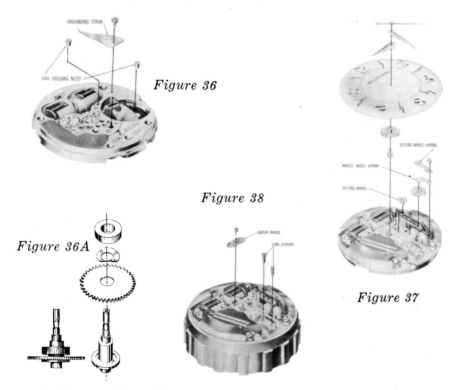

Figure 36

Figure 38

Figure 36A

Figure 37

9. Remove the setting wheel.

CAUTION: If train is spun forward or forced backwards in removing or replacing the hands, the indexing mechanism will be damaged.

Assembly

1. Moisten center pinion staff with oil and replace cannon pinion. Cannon pinion should be rather tight on the center post; hand clutch traction is taken up by a spring washer on the center post between a friction bushing and the otherwise loose-riding center wheel. (Figure 36a.)

2. Replace the setting wheel.

3. Replace the minute wheel.

4. Replace the setting wheel spring, minute wheel spring and setting wheel screw.

5. Replace the hour wheel.

6. Replace the dial.

7. Replace the hands.

8. Replace the two dial holding screws.

9. Replace the ground strap.

1. Place movement in dial up position on holder.

2. Remove shock bridge, which is held by one shock bridge

screw (Figure 38).

3. Remove the two tuning fork screws.

  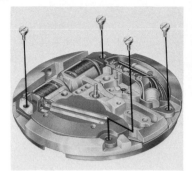

Figure 39   Figure 40   Figure 41

Removing and Repairing Coil and Fork Assembly

Removing

1. Place movement in dial up position on holder.

2. Remove shock bridge, which is held by one shock bridge screw (Figure 38).

3. Remove the two tuning fork screws.

4. Place movement in dial down position on movement holder (Figure 39).

4a. Remove safety bridge (see Figure 29).

5. Loosen index guard screw and turn index guard away from index wheel. Do not remove guard when turning it out, and be careful not to damage index and pawl fingers. Now tighten the screw.

6. Using a metal punch, disengage tuning fork by tapping on its base through hole provided in pillar plate.

7. Pick up movement and holder; invert them so movement is on bottom; remove holder and place it under movement.

8. Lift fork at base and carefully rotate it upwards until it is self-supporting in a vertical position (Figure 40).

9. Remove coil lead retainer plate, which is held by two screws.

10. As shown in Figure 41, lower the fork carefully, but do not force it down.

11. Remove the four coil form screws.

12. Without turning over movement, remove holder from bottom. Nested side of holder (Figure 27) is placed over movement and rotated until locating key of movement holder engages notch at edge of pillar plate. Invert complete assembly. Pillar plate must be firmly seated in movement holder.

13. Use pegwood stick to push down on coil assembly at various points to disengage coil and fork assembly from pillar plate

(Figure 42). Nested holder is designed to receive tuning fork and coil assembly without permitting index finger to touch opening in pillar plate during removal.

14. Movement can then be removed from movement holder. Coil and fork assembly should be left in place in movement holder. If it is necessary to remove them for cleaning or replace-

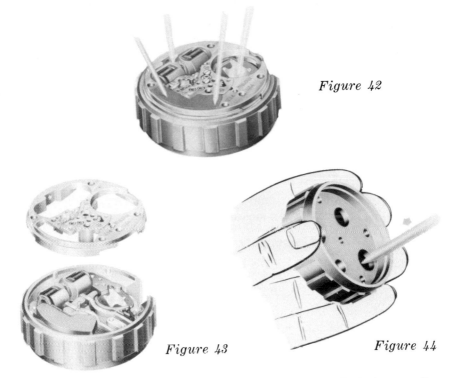

Figure 42

Figure 43

Figure 44

ment, the coils can be disassembled from the fork by gently spreading the coils.

(Some models of Accutron do not have a coil lead retainer plate. Disassembly is easier, and only these steps must be followed: 1, 2, 11, 3, 4, 5, 6, 13 and 14.)

Replacing

1. Place coil and fork assembly into prepared slots in movement holder (Figure 43).

2. Position pillar plate over assembly. Be sure that notch in pillar plate engages key in movement holder.

3. Hold movement holder as shown in Figure 44, so pillar plate will not drop out; turn over and press through holes in back to partially seat assembly in pillar plate.

4. Transfer pillar plate and coil and fork assembly from one side of movement holder to the other, placing it in dial-up posi-

tion.

5. Press down firmly on coil form only, to make sure it is completely and evenly seated in pillar plate (Figure 41).

6. Replace the four coil form screws.

7. Lift base of fork to vertical position and replace coil lead retainer plate and screws (Figure 40).

8. Lower fork carefully and press firmly into place. Apply pressure only at tongue of fork—avoid conflict with tines.

9. Replace the two tuning fork screws as shown in Figure 38.

10. Replace shock bridge screws. Check to see that fork is free to vibrate and coils fit into cups on the end of tuning fork tines without touching them. Nothing should be in contact with the tine at any point.

11. Replace dial and hands, replace ground strap and screw.

(For models of Accutron with no coil lead retainer plate, follow these steps in assembling; 1, 2, 3, 4, 5, 6, 9, and 10.)

Cleaning the Accutron

(The following additional disassembly and assembly steps should be taken only when cleaning is necessary.)

Disassembly for Cleaning

1. Remove pawl adjusting bridge and finger assembly by removing two screws shown in Figure 45. Pawl bridge cam is not threaded and will come out with the bridge. Care should be taken not to bend the pawl finger.

2. Remove the two Duofix cap jewels by applying horizontal pressure to the closed side of the U-shaped spring, allowing lip of spring to emerge from under bezel. Spring can then be tipped up, and jewels removed.

3. Remove center second chaton which is held by two chaton screws.

4. Remove center second pinion and washer by grasping with tweezers and lifting out through hole in train bridge.

5. Remove lower jewel plate, which is held by one screw as shown in Figure 46.

Cleaning

Ultrasonic equipment is preferred in cleaning the Accutron. Treat it as you would any very fine watch. However, the electronic circuit, tuning fork and pawl-adjusting bridge should not be cleaned in a machine because of the possible danger to such delicate parts. The fork, coil and bridge may be satisfactorily cleaned by dipping them in a "benzine cup" and then drying with clean tissue paper. Do not allow metal chips or filings which may be in the cleaning basket or cup to become attached magnetically to the magnets on the tuning fork. Inspect the watch for such chips carefully; and if they are present, remove them by dabbing the magnets with masking tape.

Assembly after Cleaning

1. Oil all train wheel pivots and cap jewels. *Caution*: Do not oil the index wheel teeth or index or pawl jewels.

2. Replace lower jewel plate as shown in Figure 46.

3. Replace center second pinion and washer.

4. Replace center second chaton and its two screws.

5. Replace the two Duofix cap jewels.

6. Replace pawl bridge cam. Do not push it all the way in.

7. Slide forked end of the pawl adjusting bridge under the head of the bridge, being careful not to damage the cam and position the pawl adjusting pawl finger. Replace the two screws.

8. Turn index guard back into position. Do not move it so far that it bends or touches the pawl finger. When it is positioned (Figure 35) secure index guard screw.

9. Replace safety bridge and screw.

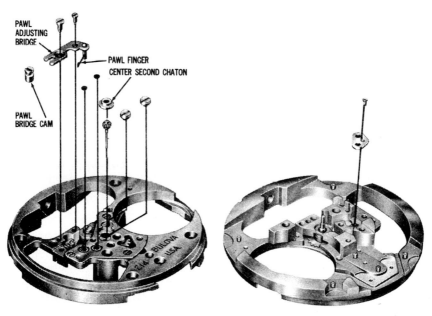

PAWL ADJUSTING BRIDGE

PAWL FINGER

CENTER SECOND CHATON

PAWL BRIDGE CAM

Figure 45   *Figure 46*

ACCUTRON
(218 SERIES)

Although Accutron's new 218 series is different from the 214, some repair procedures are alike. Therefore, this section will be treated as a continuation of the Accutron instruction.

Replacing The Power Cell

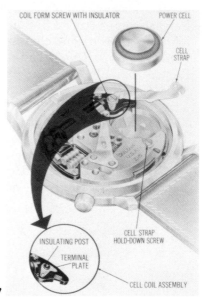

FIGURE 47

a. Remove case back, using a suitable case wrench to unscrew the locking-ring.

b. Loosen coil form screw slightly.

c. Loosen cell strap hold-down screw, swing cell strap out and remove Power Cell as shown *(see Figure 47)*.

d. Remove coil form screw (with insulator) and cell strap. Inspect (with loupe) under-surface of cell strap for foreign matter which may affect electrical contact with Power Cell. If necessary, clean with an eraser and dip-rinse.

e. With the cell strap off, check that the insulating post of the cell coil assembly has not been damaged through improper installation of a Power Cell; attach cell strap by loosely installing coil form screw (with its insulator) through cell strap, making certain cell strap is correctly positioned around the insulating post of the cell coil assembly.

f. Install the Power Cell with imprinted side down *(see Figure 47)*, reposition cell strap under the hold-down screw and secure screws.

g. Check that case gasket is properly positioned; replace case back and tighten locking-ring.

NOTE: If sweep-second hand does not turn, be sure stem is in the normal or "in" position. If so, tap the case lightly at "3" or "9" to start tuning fork vibrating.

Regulation:

As in the 214, the basic accuracy of this model is within a few seconds a day. Gains or losses of a minute or more a week indicate the need for repair, not regulation. For instructions on regulating Accutrons, turn to pages 114-115. A pointed pegwood can move the pronged regulator.

Removing Movement From Case

Pull stem **out** (setting position).

Loosen setting lever screw 2 turns. *(See Figure 48.)*

Withdraw stem.

Remove movement from case and place in movement holder.

Insert stem and tighten setting lever screw.

CAUTION: Do not push stem beyond point of engagement with pin on setting lever. (See Special Points, item 2.)

Replacing Movement In Case

Pull stem **out** (setting position).

Loosen setting lever screw 2 turns. *(See Figure 49.)*

Withdraw stem.

Replace movement in case.

Lubricate crown gasket with a good quality stem grease.

Insert stem and tighten setting lever screw.

FIGURE 48

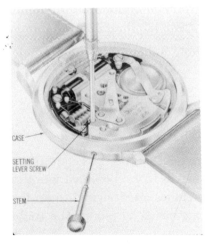

FIGURE 49

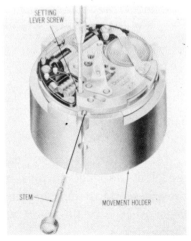

CAUTION: Do not push stem beyond point of engagement with pin on setting lever. (See Special Points, item 2.)

Replace gasket and case back. Secure locking ring for water tightness.

Check regulation.

Repair Of The Basic Movement

The tools needed are a triple-purpose electric test set *(Figure 25, page 121)*, a movement holder *(Figure 50)* and a collet adjusting tool *(Figure 51)*. The test meter provides an accurate source for the reduced voltages required for the adjustment of the 214 and 218 indexing mechanisms. (The two voltages are not the same.)

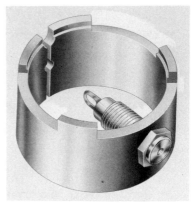

FIGURE 50

FIGURE 51

Timing Machines:

Tuning fork watches can only be recorded on equipment especially designed to pick up the signals from these fast vibrating timepieces. Most modern timing machines are designed to do this. Older ones may be fitted with attachments to record the tuning fork watches.

136

TROUBLE SHOOTING CHART

SYMPTOM	PROBABLE CAUSES (In order of probability)	DIAGNOSIS PROCEDURE	CORRECTIVE ACTION REQUIRED
GAINING OR LOSING A FEW SECONDS PER DAY	Abnormal condition of use or improper regulation.	No diagnosis required.	Regulate pages 114 to 115.
IRREGULAR DAY-TO-DAY RATE (gains a few seconds per day, loses a few seconds the next, etc.)	Inaccurate source of time for checking Accutron rate.	Determine source of time used for checking performance.	Recommend (a) checking performance over 1 month period in keeping with guarantee, or (b) use of accurate time source for daily checking.
GAINING OR LOSING EXCESSIVELY (minutes per week)	1. Hands rub or catch slightly.	Check crystal clearance. Inspect for adequate clearance between hands and between hands and dial markers.	Adjust hand clearance. Be sure to pull out crown during adjustment to avoid damaging indexing mechanism.
	2. Poor contact between cell strap & Power Cell.	Inspect Power Cell and cell strap for an adherent deposit of dried electrolyte which may sometimes "push" the cell strap away from the Power Cell.	Clean and replace Power Cell and cell strap, as described, ("d" & "e"). page 134.
	3. Indexing mechanism out of adjustment.	Check adjustment of indexing mechanism. pages 140 to 143.	Adjust indexing mechanism, if necessary. pages 140 to 143.
	4. Mechanical interference with free vibrations of fork.	Check movement current page 144. If current is above OK range, rotate index finger collet to disengage jewel from index wheel. If current remains above OK range, fork may be blocked.	Remove blockage. Readjust indexing mechanism.
	5. Train partially blocked.	If movement current was above normal in step 4 (above) but current is OK with index mechanism disengaged, train is partially blocked. Check train freedom page 145.	Remove blockage. Readjust indexing mechanism. pages 140 to 143.
	6. Damaged teeth on index wheel.	See "Special Points" page 139 item 3.	Replace index wheel (disassembly procedures 1-4, page 146 and reassembly procedures 6-8, pages 149 to 151). Check adjustment of indexing mechanism
STOPPED no hum	1. Exhausted Power Cell.	Open case, remove Power Cell and check its voltage page 144. If voltage is low, Power Cell is exhausted.	Replace Power Cell page 134.
	2. Open drive coil.	Check movement current page 144. If no current, one of the drive coils is "open."	Identify defective coil page 145 and remove same (disassembly procedures 1-5, pages 146 to 149 and reassembly procedures 5-8, pages 149 to 151. Readjust indexing mechanism
	3. Mechanical blockage of tuning fork.	If movement current is above OK range in step 2 (above), rotate index finger collet to disengage jewel from index wheel. If current remains above OK range, fork may be blocked.	Remove blockage. Readjust indexing mechanism pages 140 to 143.
	4. Faulty electronic circuit.	If movement current is high and tuning fork is not blocked, electronic circuit is faulty.	Replace component coil assembly (disassembly procedures 1-5, pages 146 to 149 and reassembly procedures 5-8, pages 149 to 151. Readjust indexing mechanism

SYMPTOM	PROBABLE CAUSES (In order of probability)	DIAGNOSIS PROCEDURE	CORRECTIVE ACTION REQUIRED
STOPPED Sweep second hand does not turn but fork hums.	1. Crown in setting ("out") position.	Check to see if crown is pressed in.	Press crown "in."
	2. Power Cell voltage low.	If crown is "in," open case, remove Power Cell and check its voltage page 144. If voltage is low, Power Cell is exhausted.	Replace Power Cell page 134.
	3. Hack mechanism out of adjustment.	Remove movement from case and place in movement holder page 136. Check adjustment of hack mechanism page 140.	Adjust hack mechanism page 140.
	4. Indexing mechanism out of adjustment.	Check adjustment of indexing mechanism pages 140 to 143.	Adjust indexing mechanism. Pages 140 to 143.
	5. Mechanical interference with free, vibrations of fork.	Check movement current page 144. If current is above OK range rotate index finger collet to disengage jewel from index wheel. If current remains above OK range fork may may be blocked.	Remove blockage. Readjust indexing mechanism pages 140 to 143.
	6. Mechanical blockage of train.	If movement current was above normal in step 5 (above) but current is OK with index mechanism disengaged, train is partially blocked. Check train freedom page 145.	Remove blockage. Readjust indexing mechanism pages 140 to 143.
	7. Dirt in tooth of index wheel.	If above checks prove negative, connect test set with switch in "read microamperes" position. With crown "in," tap movement holder at 3 or 9 o'clock position with finger to increase fork amplitude, while observing closely with loupe. If index wheel rotates once, then stops again, there may be dirt in index wheel teeth.	Remove index wheel (disassembly procedures 1-4, pages 146 to 149. Clean wheel and reassemble. Readjust indexing mechanism pages 140 to 143.
	8. Damaged teeth on index wheel.	If test in step 7 (above) is positive but is not corrected by cleaning index wheel, index wheel teeth have been damaged. See "Special Points" page 139 item 3.	Replace index wheel (disassembly procedures 1-4, pages 146 to 149 and reassembly procedures 6-8, pages 149 to 151. Readjust indexing mechanism pages 140 to 143.
STOPPED Hour and minute hands stopped but sweep second hand turns.	1. Hands catch.	Inspect for adequate clearance between hands and between hands and dial markers.	Adjust hand clearance. Be sure to pull out crown during adjustment to avoid damaging indexing mechanism.
	2. Stoppage in dial train.	If hand clearances are satisfactory, remove dial and hands. Inspect for foreign matter or other stoppage interfering with free turning of dial train.	Remove blockage.

Special Points for the ACCUTRON Repairman

The ACCUTRON movement, being completely different from conventional watch movements, requires different techniques in its repair. Otherwise, it may be damaged by improper procedures on the part of the repairman. For example, turning the hands or the gear train (in either direction) with the hack lever disengaged, will damage the index wheel teeth or the index and pawl fingers. The repairman's attention is called to the following special points:

1. Removing or Replacing Hands

Always pull crown **out** (setting position) before touching the hands for any reason.

2. Replacing Stem

As with conventional watches, the stem should preferably be pulled "out" (setting position) before loosening the setting lever screw to remove the stem. In replacing the stem, if it is pushed in, beyond the point of engagement with the pin on the setting lever, the hack lever may be depressed. In this instance, turning the crown will damage the indexing mechanism. For this reason, **do not push the stem in beyond the point where the stem groove may be engaged by the setting lever pin, before tightening the setting lever screw.**

3. Index Wheel

The teeth on the index wheel will not wear away in normal use, nor can they be damaged as a result of any accident, when the movement is enclosed in its case (with the crystal intact). The index wheel can only be damaged by improper handling on the part of the repairman. If it is suspected that the teeth on the index wheel have been damaged, the most practical solution is to replace it, since visual examination will rarely disclose the damage — because of the size of these tiny teeth. However, proper diagnostic inspection of the index wheel teeth can be accomplished with a 100x to 200x monocular microscope using sub-stage illumination.

4. Lubrication

Do not lubricate the teeth of the index wheel, or the index or pawl jewels.

5. Circuit

The use of electrical test equipment or procedures other than those recommended, should be avoided. In particular, circuit elements can be damaged by the use of an ohmmeter for testing the circuit.

6. Magnetism

Never demagnetize an ACCUTRON movement or expose it to high-strength magnetic fields (permanent magnets, for example).

7. Magnets Partially Demagnetized

Diagnosis procedures in the preceding servicing instructions have not covered the identification of trouble caused by demagnetized tuning fork magnets, for reasons of simplification. Experience has shown that such trouble is very rare. If the movement current is within the "OK" area of the scale on the Test Set, the magnets are satisfactorily magnetized.

If the tuning fork magnets have lost most of their magnetism, the tuning fork will fail to vibrate and the Test Set will indicate a very high current — normally interpreted as due to a faulty electronic circuit. If the magnets have lost only a portion of their magnetism, the tuning fork may vibrate but the Test Set will indicate that the current is above the "OK" area of the scale. In each of these instances, if an excessively high current (and/or failure of the tuning fork to vibrate) cannot be corrected by replacing the complete coil assembly — try substituting a different tuning fork.

If the tuning fork magnets have been demagnetized — the tuning fork assembly must be returned to Bulova for remagnetizing.

8. Adjustment of Indexing Mechanism

It is *always* good practice to check the adjustment of the indexing mechanism *after* replacing the dial and hands. This is because the adjustment of the indexing mechanism can change as a result of the slightest turning of the center second pinion when the hand is applied. For the same reason, whenever an ACCUTRON timepiece is received for repair with the crystal missing, always check the adjustment and operation of the indexing mechanism, which could have been deranged by any interference with the exposed sweep second hand.

Indexing Mechanism — Inspection and Adjustment

The checking and adjustment of the ACCUTRON indexing mechanism is extremely important to its operation. This is accomplished by closely controlling the alignment and the depth of engagement of the index and pawl jewels and their interrelation. Details of the step by step procedure necessary to properly accomplish these adjustments are to be performed in sequence, as follows:

NOTE: Perform hack mechanism inspection and adjustment before the following steps.

1. Check that stem is in (running position). Remove casing spring (2 screws) and power cell .

2. The lower surfaces of the index and pawl jewels must be parallel to their respective fingers, as shown in Figure 53. Correction of

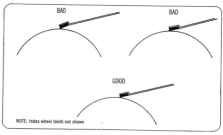

FIGURE 53

140

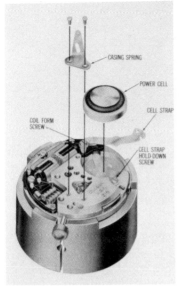

CASING SPRING

POWER CELL

COIL FORM
SCREW

CELL STRAP

CELL STRAP
HOLD-DOWN
SCREW

FIGURE 52

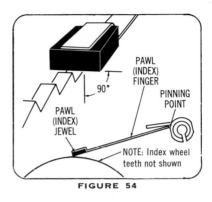

PAWL
(INDEX)
FINGER

PINNING
POINT

90°

PAWL
(INDEX)
JEWEL

NOTE: Index wheel
teeth not shown

FIGURE 54

this alignment is rarely required. It can usually be accomplished, if necessary, without breaking the cement attaching the jewel to the finger by exercising watchmaking care. Grasp the finger with tweezers, close to the jewel, and press lightly on the end of the jewel or finger in the proper direction with pegwood, to correct the alignment of jewel and finger.

For the proper operation, the two fingers must be straight. Obviously, when the fingers are unstressed (disengaged from wheel), there will be a slight curve.

Both of the jewels must be perpendicular to the wheel. Either jewel can be made perpendicular to the plane of the index wheel by grasping the jewel finger close to its pinning point and twisting slightly. *(See Figure 54.)* Centering the index and/or pawl jewel is accomplished by alignment of the respective post. Gently stress the index or pawl post by grasping or pushing the end of the post with tweezers or a suitable screwdriver. *(See Figure 55.)* This very slight bending of the post will raise or lower the index or pawl jewel in relation to the index wheel. Exercise normal watchmaking care in readjusting the various parts of the ACCUTRON indexing mechanism.

3. Rotate index finger collet until index jewel completely disengages from index wheel. Observe gap between index gage and index finger.

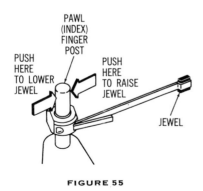

PAWL
(INDEX)
FINGER
POST

PUSH
HERE
TO LOWER
JEWEL

PUSH
HERE
TO RAISE
JEWEL

JEWEL

FIGURE 55

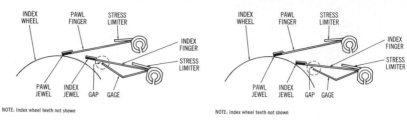

NOTE: Index wheel teeth not shown

FIGURE 56

NOTE: Index wheel teeth not shown

FIGURE 57

(See Figure 56.) The gage must not touch the finger, but should preferably be very close, say within one index finger thickness. This, as you will see, will make it easier to perform step 4. If gap does not meet requirements, bend index gage at its attached end until the proper gap is obtained.

4. Use collet adjusting tool to rotate index collet, bring index jewel into wheel until the gap is larger than it was in step 3 by 1 to 1½ index jewel thicknesses. If the gap in step 3 was less than the thickness of the index finger, for practical purposes this gap should be increased to about 1½ jewel thicknesses at the completion of collet adjustment. *(See Figure 57.)*

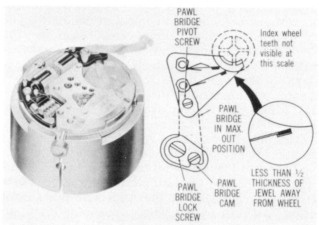

FIGURE 58

5. Observe the stress limiters on index and pawl fingers. *(See Figure 57.)* Check that no more than 1/3 of the length of the stress limiter is in contact with the index or pawl finger. Also, check that end of stress limiter is no more than 3 thicknesses of the stress limiter away from index or pawl finger. If adjustment is necessary, use tweezers to bend stress limiter; then repeat steps 3 and 4.

6. Loosen pawl bridge lock screw slightly; leave pawl bridge pivot screw tight.

7. Rotate pawl bridge cam until pawl bridge is in its maximum clockwise position (maximum position in the direction to disengage pawl jewel from index wheel). *(See Figure 58.)* The pawl

jewel should not be touching the index wheel, and not more than one-half its thickness away from the wheel. This distance may be adjusted using the collet adjusting tool.

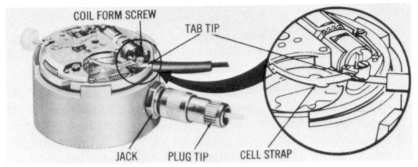

FIGURE 59

8. Insert plug tip of Test Set lead into the jack of the movement holder. Insert tab tip of other lead of Test Set under strap as shown in Figure 59. With Power Cell in the nest of Test Set, turn rotary switch to "LOW AMPLITUDE" position. If tuning fork does not begin to vibrate, an excess current reading will be indicated on meter of Test Set. Should this occur, tap movement holder lightly and fork will start. Current reading will then drop to the lower end of "OK" area, or slightly below.

9. Rotate the pawl bridge cam VERY SLOWLY in either direction (since it was at its maximum distance away, rotating either clockwise or counterclockwise will move the pawl jewel toward the wheel) until movement begins to run. This can be seen merely by watching the wheels that are visible. TURN THE CAM FARTHER IN THE SAME DIRECTION UNTIL THE TRAIN STOPS, AND THEN CONTINUE STILL FARTHER UNTIL YOU REACH THE POINT WHERE IT STARTS AGAIN AND CONTINUES TO RUN (Momentary hesitation permissible).

10. Tighten the pawl bridge lock screw and check the tightness of the pawl bridge pivot screw, to assure that the bridge is rigidly clamped in position. The ACCUTRON train should continue to run (Test Set switch at "LOW AMPLITUDE" position). If it does not, the adjustment must be made again (steps 7 through 10).

11. Disconnect the Test Set from the movement.

Testing 218 Power Cell

1. Place the Power Cell (with yellow seal up) in nest of Test Set.

2. Turn rotary switch on Test Set to "CHECK POWER CELL" position.

3. Read Power Cell voltage on right-hand scale. The voltage reading should be in the "OK" area of scale (1.25 to 1.45 volts). If it is, Power Cell is in satisfactory operating condition.

NOTE: Poor electrical contact between Power Cell and Test Set will cause either a low reading or a wavering indication of cell voltage. It can be readily avoiced by making certain that Power Cell surfaces and contacting points of the Test Set nest and clip are clean. Rubbing or twisting a suspected cell between the contacts while checking voltage is good practice. A wavering reading of voltage is always an indication of poor contact, not an indication of a bad cell. Testing should always be done with the authorized ACCUTRON Test Set or with a high-resistance voltmeter (having not less than 10,000 ohms per volt sensitivity), such as the ACCUTRON Power Cell Tester.*

CAUTION: Never use substitute cells in place of the genuine "ACCUTRON 218" Power Cell. Though other cells may look the same, they will not reliably operate this model timepiece and may, in some instances, seriously damage the movement. The only correct Power Cell has "ACCUTRON 218" imprint.

Testing Electronic Circuit

The following procedure is performed with the Power Cell in the nest of the Test Set and the movement positioned in the movement holder.

1. Insert plug tip of Test Set lead into the jack of the movement holder. *(See Figure 59.)*

2. Insert tab tip of other lead of Test Set under cell strap as shown in Figure 59.

3. Turn rotary switch on Test Set to "READ MICRO-AMPERES" position. The Test Set meter should give a reading of current on left-hand scale. (It may be necessary to tap movement lightly to start tuning fork vibrating after connecting Test Set leads.)

4. Observe current reading. If reading is in the "OK" area of scale (8.0 to 10.0 microamperes for the dialed movement with indexing mechanism engaged) electronic circuit is operating satisfactorily. Bare fork operation (that is pillar plate, tuning fork and coils only) may give a current reading as low as 6 microamperes.

Identifying Defective Assembly

This procedure is intended to identify which coil assembly is defective, when a check of the movement current results in an excessive or a zero current reading, indicating improper functioning of the electronic circuit.

excessive current

If the tuning fork is not blocked (can vibrate freely) yet will not start when the movement is tapped, excessive current (substantially above 10 microamperes) is usually an indication that the component coil assembly is defective and must be replaced.

zero current

Assuming the Power Cell has been checked and the Test Set properly connected to the movement, yet the meter indicates zero current, perform the following simple test:

Remove the plug-tip lead from the jack in the movement holder and touch it to the lead strap screw between the two coil assemblies. The defective (open) coil may be identified by whether the current indicated by the meter:

a. Remains zero — Replace the cell coil assembly

b. Becomes excessive — Replace the component coil assembly

Checking the Train for Freedom

This check is used to determine whether there is any mechanical blockage of the gear train.

The most sensitive and convenient method of checking the train freedom is to pluck, or "twang" the tine of the tuning fork to which the index finger is attached. When this is done, the fork will vibrate for a few seconds and this motion will be transmitted to the train — if it is not blocked.

The motion of the train can easily be seen by watching any of the wheels at the time that the fork is being plucked. If no motion of the gears is apparent when the fork is plucked, this is evidence of a blocked train, assuming that the indexing linkage has already been checked.

The freedom of the train may also be checked by simply moving one of the wheels with a tweezers or needle with both pawl and index collets rotated to disengage the respective jewels from the index wheel.

Hack Mechanism — Inspection and Adjustment

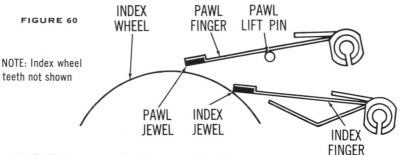

FIGURE 60

1. Pull stem **out** (setting position).

2. Pawl jewel should be from ½ to 1 jewel thickness away from index wheel. *(See Figure 60.)* If necessary adjust by bending pawl lift pin.

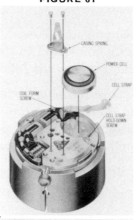

FIGURE 61

Removing Power Cell and Casing Spring

a. Loosen cell strap hold down screw and coil form screw. *(See Figure 61.)*

b. Turn cell strap counterclockwise and remove power cell.

c. Remove casing spring (2 screws).

Disengaging Index and Pawl Fingers

a. Push stem **in** (running condition).

b. Use collet adjusting tool to rotate index and pawl fingers away from index wheel. *(See Figure 62.)*

FIGURE 62

146

Removing Train Bridge and Train Wheels

a. Remove train bridge (4 screws).

b. Remove train wheels. *(See Figure 63.)*

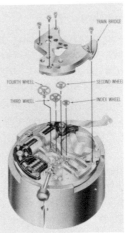

FIGURE 63

Removing Tuning Fork and Coil Assemblies

a. Rotate pawl finger assembly clockwise 180 degrees to clear tuning fork and pawl bridge pivot screw.

b. Remove tuning fork and coil assemblies (6 screws). *(See Figure 64.)*

CAUTION: Do not pry at base of tuning fork. Use a punch (bottom) to push tongue of tuning fork through push-off hole on dial side.

c. Note position of fork spacers. Colors denote different thicknesses.

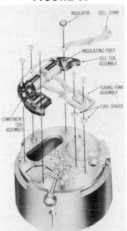

FIGURE 64

Removing Pawl Bridge and Hack Lever

a. Remove pawl bridge and cam (2 screws).

b. Remove hack lever and hack lever spring *(see Figure 65)*.

c. Remove yoke, detach lever spring and clutch lever.

d. Remove setting wheel and minute wheel.

e. Remove fourth bridge (2 screws) and center wheel assembly.

f. Remove set lever screw, set lever, stem and clutch wheel.

g. Remove center-second brake spring and remove ground plate *(see Figure 66)*.

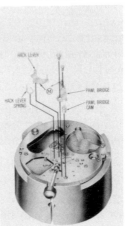

FIGURE 65

147

Cleaning

FIGURE 66

Separate all cap jewels in jeweling devices with spring-held cap jewels from pillar plate and train bridge. After cleaning, replace cap jewel assemblies.

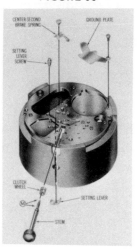

Ultrasonic equipment is necessary for cleaning the ACCUTRON movement. The ACCUTRON movement should be treated exactly as any fine watch movement, with one exception. The electronic circuit, the tuning fork and the pawl bridge should not be cleaned in ultrasonic equipment, because of the possibility of damage to delicate parts.

The tuning fork, coils, and pawl bridge can be cleaned satisfactorily by merely dipping into a "benzine cup" and then placing on a tissue to dry.

Care should be taken to prevent metal chips, which may be present in the cleaning cup or on the bench, from being attracted to the permanent magnets on the tines of the tuning fork. Inspect the fork carefully after cleaning, and if this has occurred, any particles that are clinging to the magnets can be removed with masking tape or "Rodico". NO PARTICLES SHOULD BE LEFT CLINGING TO FORK MAGNETS.

The center wheel assembly (cannon pinion with center wheel) should not be taken apart, but cleaned as a unit. After cleaning, the wheel should not be rotated until properly lubricated. (See reassembly instruction.)

The index wheel requires special handling care in cleaning to prevent damage to the index teeth. For this purpose, it is necessary to use a suitable tool to grasp the index wheel pivots when immersing the index wheel in the ultrasonic cleaner. NEVER HANDLE THE INDEX WHEEL BY THE RIM. GRASP THE PINION ONLY.

A suitable holding tool for cleaning the index wheel can easily be fabricated by modifying an ordinary pair of watchmaker's tweezers made of brass or other non-magnetic material, as follows:

1. Spot drill the insides of the tweezer tips as shown in the upper section of Figure 67.

2. Bend a piece of stiff wire around the tweezers and form the wire so that it can be used as a clamp. One end of the wire should be placed between the tweezer tongs.

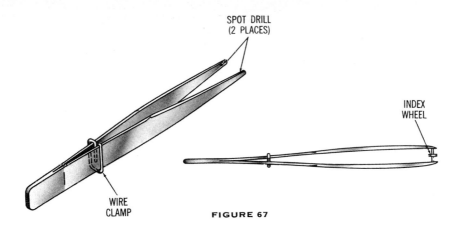

SPOT DRILL
(2 PLACES)

INDEX
WHEEL

WIRE
CLAMP

FIGURE 67

3. Check that wire clamp locks tweezer tips progressively closer together as clamp is pushed towards the tips.

NOTE: Authorized Material Distributors can supply, at nominal cost, a special Index Wheel Holder *(see Figure 67).*

Lubrication

In the following reassembly procedures, important lubrication instructions are required for the Series 218 ACCUTRON. These are as follows:

(V) Moebius OL219 — Synta Visco Lube

(M) Moebius OL207 — Special Lubricant with Molybdenum Disulfide

REASSEMBLY

a. Replace clutch wheel, stem, setting lever, and setting lever screw.

b. Lubricate stem square and pilot (M) . Use lubricant sparingly.

c. Replace center-second brake spring (1 screw).

d. Replace ground plate (1 screw).

(M) Moebius OL207 — Special Lubricant with Molybdenum Disulfide

Replacing Center Wheel Assembly and Fourth Bridge

a. Lubricate sparingly the center wheel assembly and center tube. (M)

b. Replace center wheel assembly.

c. Replace fourth wheel bridge and screws.

d. Lubricate minute wheel pivot and setting wheel post (M) . Use lubricant sparingly.

e. Replace minute wheel and setting wheel.

f. Replace clutch lever and clutch lever spring.

g. Replace yoke (1 screw).

Lubricate yoke Ⓜ

Ⓜ Moebius OL207 — Special Lubricant with Molybdenum Disulfide

CAUTION: If clutch lever is replaced upside down, damage to indexing mechanism can result.

Replacing Hack Lever and Pawl Bridge *(See Figure 65)*

a. Replace hack lever.

b. Replace hack lever spring with short leg toward lever, as shown.

c. Lubricate Stem pilot Ⓜ where it touches hack lever. Use lubricant sparingly.

d. Replace pawl bridge and cam (2 screws).

Ⓜ Moebius OL207 — Special Lubricant with Molybdenum Disulfide

Replacing Tuning Fork and Coil Assemblies *(See Figure 64)*

a. Replace tuning fork and coil assemblies (6 screws).

NOTE: Tuning fork spacers are used to center fork tines between pillar plate and train bridge.

b. Replace cell strap.

NOTE: Check that cell strap is properly centered on pilot of coil form before tightening screw.

c. Rotate the pawl finger assembly counterclockwise to bring the pawl finger adjacent to the lift pin.

Replacing Train Wheels and Train Bridge *(See Figure 63)*

a. Oil all cap jewels in pillar plate and train bridge Ⓥ . Oil sparingly. Do not flood jewels.

b. Push stem in (running position).

c. Replace train wheels.

CAUTION: MAKE CERTAIN THAT PAWL FINGER HAS BEEN ROTATED AS PER STEP C, REPLACING TUNING FORK AND COIL ASSEMBLIES (PREVIOUS SECTION), TO AVOID DAMAGE TO PAWL FINGER. IN ADDITION, MAKE CERTAIN THAT BOTH THE INDEX AND PAWL FINGERS ARE DIS-ENGAGED FROM THE INDEX WHEEL BEFORE PERFORM-ING THE NEXT STEP.

d. Replace train bridge (4 screws).

e. Oil fourth lower jewel Ⓥ (from dial side).

f. Check wheel train for freedom with tweezers or needle.

Ⓥ Moebius OL219 — Synta Visco Lube

Replacing Hour Wheel, Dial, and Hands

a. Replace hour wheel and dial washer.

b. Replace dial (2 screws).

c. Pull stem out (setting position).

d. Replace hands.

NOTE: It is necessary to support the center second upper cap jewel on a proper fitting stump in a staking set when replacing center-second hand.

e. Perform hack mechanism adjustment, page 146.

f. Perform index mechanism adjustment, pages 140 to 142.

Replacing Casing Spring and Power Cell *(See Figure 61)*

a. Replace casing spring (2 screws).

b. Replace power cell (imprinted side down, yellow seal up).

c. Tighten cell strap and coil form screws.

Replacing Movement in Case

See page 135.

Regulation Following Repair

After the movement has been replaced in the case, always check regulation (adjust if necessary) to assure that the rate of the *cased* timepiece is approximately two seconds per day slow, in dial up position. The most convenient method is to use the Rate Recorder. Otherwise, be certain that an *accurate* time source is used for checking true 24-hour rate.

Repair of Hour Setting and Date Mechanisms in Model 2185

All information and instructions covered in 218 Series are also applicable to Model 2185, with the following exceptions:

Details for removing and replacing movement in case, disassembly, lubricating, and reassembly of the hour setting and date mechanism are given in the accompanying illustrations.

When ordering replacement parts, be sure to indicate that the parts are for Model 2185.

EXPLODED VIEWS MODEL 2185

(All other parts same as basic Series 218)

123	Foot	623	Foot
208	Clutch Wheel	625	Planetary Hour Wheel Assembly
305	Date and Set Bridge Screw	630	Geneva Wheel
321	Date Corrector Detent Screw	631	Cam Assembly
451	Cam Screw	633	Geneva Wheel Stop Disc
452	Spring Washer	634	Geneva Wheel Spring
569	Date Corrector	635	Cam Gear
570	Date Corrector Detent	636	Transfer Gear Assembly
571	Date Bridge	637	Hour Setting Wheel
572	Date Indicator Detent	640	Intermediate Wheel Assembly
573	Date Indicator Detent Spring	641	Drive Gear Assembly
574	Date Trip Wheel Assembly	642	Cam Spring
576	Date Indicator	643	Cam Spring Screw
579	Center Wheel Assembly	644	Setting Bridge Assembly
580	Minute Wheel Assembly	648	Hour Setting Stem
581	Date Trip Arm		(Not Shown)
582	Date Trip Spring	649	Stem Locking Spring

152

Exploded View Model 2185

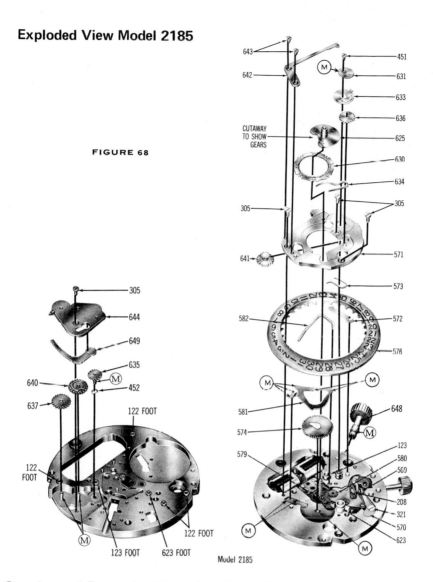

FIGURE 68

643
642
451
M
631
633
636
CUTAWAY
TO SHOW
GEARS
625
630
634
305
305
641
571
573
582
572
576
305
644
649
635
640
M
452
637
122 FOOT
581
648
M
574
123
579
580
569
122
FOOT
208
321
570
M
122 FOOT
M
623
123 FOOT   623 FOOT
M

Model 2185

Opening and Removing Movement From Case *(See Figure 69)*

a. Remove locking ring with the use of a special ACCUTRON locking ring wrench.

b. After removing case back and gasket, depress stem locking spring #649 and withdraw hour setting stem #648 *(see Figure 69).*

c. Pull time setting stem #176 "out" (setting position).

d. Loosen setting lever screw two turns and withdraw time setting stem #176.

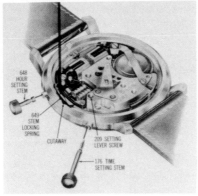

FIGURE 69

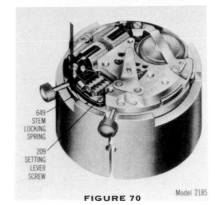

FIGURE 70

Model 2185

e. Remove movement from case and place movement in holder *(see Figure 70)*.

f. Insert time setting stem #176 and tighten setting lever screw.

CAUTION: Do not push stem beyond point of engagement with stem pin on setting lever. (See Special Points, Item 2.)

NOTE: Unless hour setting operation must be checked, do not replace hour setting stem #648 at this time.

To insert hour setting stem #648, depress stem locking spring #649 and insert stem *(see Figure 70)*.

When checking hour setting mechanism operation with movement removed from case, carefully hold and rotate hour setting stem to insure a positive engagement of teeth between hour setting stem #648 and hour setting wheel #637. Caution must be taken not to damage stem guide pin.

Replacing Movement in Case

a. If previously installed, depress stem locking spring #649 and withdraw hour setting stem #648 *(see Figure 70)*.

b. With time setting stem #176 "out" (setting position), loosen setting lever screw two turns and withdraw stem.

c. Replace movement in case.

154

d. Lubricate both hour and time setting crown gaskets with a good quality grease.

e. Insert time setting stem #176 and tighten setting lever screw.

CAUTION: Do not push stem beyond point of engagement with stem pin on setting lever.

f. Depress stem locking spring #649 and insert hour setting stem #648 *(see Figure 69)*.

g. Replace gasket and case back. Secure locking ring for water tightness.

h. Check regulation.

Removing Hour Setting Mechanism, Train Side

NOTE: Perform all necessary disassembly, train side, before proceeding with the following steps:

a. Remove setting bridge assembly #644 and screw #305.

b. Remove stem locking spring #649.

c. Remove cam gear #635 with spring washer #452, intermediate wheel assembly #640, and hour setting wheel #637.

Replacing Hour Setting Mechanism, Train Side

a. Lubricate sparingly hour setting wheel post, intermediate wheel assembly post and cam gear shaft.

b. Replace hour setting wheel #637 with intermediate wheel assembly #640 (small gear down) and cam gear #635 with spring washer #452.

c. Replace stem locking spring #649 and setting bridge assembly #644. Secure with setting bridge screw #305 and check endshake, (5/100 mm) for all three gears.

d. The remaining parts of the train side and setting mechanism are assembled as illustrated.

All points marked Ⓜ to be lubricated with Moebius OL207.

CARAVELLE
(Model 12 OTC — 12 OUCD)

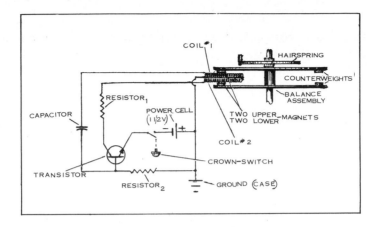

No special knowledge of electronics is required for servicing the CARAVELLE model 12 OTC movement and the service procedures, established here, take advantage of standard tools. The only equipment required, in addition to the customary "tools of the trade," is a suitable high resistance voltmeter for checking power cell voltage. For this purpose a meter having at least 20,000 ohms per volt must be used. A universal measuring instrument (ohmmeter) if available is occasionally helpful for checking the coils. The traditional operations, familiar to the watchmaker, are mentioned in this manual and the special functions are described in detail. The 12 OTC model incorporates 12 jewels and shock-absorbing devices for protection of the balance pivots. Only normal watchmaking precautions need be exercised during servicing and/or repair.

The CARAVELLE, model 12 OTC, is fitted with a positive advance indexing system actuated by the oscillating balance assembly through a jeweled pallet lever. A train of wheels and pinions (4 time and 2 dial) transmits controlled rotation to the time-of-day hands. The electronic circuit incorporates a transistor which acts as an electronic switch or gate. Magnets on the balance wheel in passing over the flat coil assembly, induce signals which turn the transistor on and off. The transistor amplifies the signal and feeds current pulses to the coil assembly to drive the 18,000 beat balance wheel electromagnetically by interaction with the magnets mounted on the balance wheel. Resistors in the printed circuit control the current to the drive coil which sustains balance motion (amplitude). When the crown is pulled out, a stop lever engages the balance assembly and a switch is opened, stopping the watch and the current in the electronic circuit. The source of power, applied through the electronic circuit direct to the balance, is a miniature silver oxide type power cell having a nominal voltage of 1.5 volts bearing the identification imprint "12 OTC". DO NOT USE A SUBSTITUTE POWER CELL. Hearing-aid batteries, having a similar external appearance, use a different electrolyte and sealing technique which may allow leakage of corrosive materials that can damage the CARAVELLE movement and negate Bulova's warranty.

The troubleshooting chart on the following pages provides a means to pinpoint malfunctions accurately and quickly by reference to four basic symptoms. The watchmaker, attempting to make repair, should refer to this chart to eliminate complicating his repair. Experience has shown the printed circuit and coils to be relatively trouble-free and, unless damaged, will rarely cause trouble. If the watch fails to function after mechanical inspection and adjustment the Coil Assembly and Circuit Assembly should be examined for obvious damage such as nicks, scratches, or broken wires. See "Faulty coil" in troubleshooting chart for test procedures and resistance value of coils.

DO NOT subject this watch to a demagnetizer. The permanent magnets in the balance assembly and lower plate are required for proper operation and may cause associated parts to become magnetized. Such magnetism will not affect timekeeping as it would in the conventional watch. The use of non-magnetic tweezers in handling parts will speed and facilitate repair.

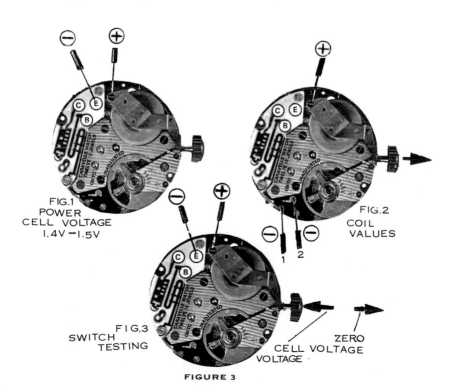

FIG.1
POWER
CELL VOLTAGE
1.4V –1.5V

FIG.2
COIL
VALUES

1   2

FIG.3
SWITCH
TESTING

CELL VOLTAGE
VOLTAGE

ZERO
CELL VOLTAGE

FIGURE 3

TROUBLESHOOTING CHART FOR 12 OTC

SYMPTOM	PROBABLE CAUSES	DIAGNOSTIC PROCEDURE	REMEDIAL ACTION
1. GAINING OR LOSING A MINIMAL AMOUNT	Improper regulation	Test the rate on a standard watch-rate recorder or "rack time"	Regulate
2. GAINING OR LOSING EXCESSIVELY	1) Low power cell voltage.	Measure power cell voltage *(Note: Cell voltage can be checked between the emitter (-) and the plate (+) with crown pushed "in". See Figure 1.)*	If voltage is less than 1.4 volts, change power cell.
	2) Low balance motion.	Determine balance motion and if mechanically correct inspect circuit.	Correct mechanical mal-adjustment and/or replace circuit.
	3) Dust or dirt in train, indexing system or Balance assembly.	Determine amplitude, see F, item 3 under Electrical System relating to damping.	If dirty or balance motion is low in flat position overhaul movement.
	4) Improper adjustment of indexing mechanism.	Check the functions of indexing mechanism.	Readjust the indexing mechanism.
	5) Knocking.	Inspect mechanical alignment of balance and associated parts. Determine balance motion.	Properly align balance and related parts. Eliminate any mechanical damping see item 3.
3. AN AUDIBLE SOUND WITH HANDS STOPPED (Second hand does not turn, but balance is oscillating)	1) Low power cell voltage.	Measure power cell voltage.	Replace power cell with new one.
	2) Damage in the indexing mechanism.	Inspect index wheel, pallet arbor pivots, and pallet stones.	Change index wheel, pallet lever or associated parts and adjust if necessary.
	3) Damaged balance wheel.	Check the gap between balance magnets and coil (movement out of the case).	Adjust the deformed balance wheel and establish proper gap. See note under "Electrical System" section.
	4) Dust or dirt in gear train, indexing mechanism and balance.	Determine balance motion and look for dirt.	If balance motion is low in flat position, overhaul the movement.
	5) Improper adjustment of indexing mechanism.	Check the functions of indexing mechanism (see Adjustment of the Indexing Mechanism).	Adjust the indexing mechanism.
4. STOPPED	1) Hands catching.	Profile viewing of hands and dial markers, check crystal condition and height.	Align hands or change crystal.
	2) Low power cell voltage.	Measure power cell voltage.	Change power cell.
	3) Damage of balance wheel, balance staff and hairspring (by violent shock).	Find interference by carefully finger turning balance wheel.	Adjust the deformed balance wheel or change balance.
	4) Mechanical interference or lint, dirt, or metal chips on magnets.	If balance wheel is blocked or does not transmit motion to sweep-second pinion when turned in both directions, inspect gear train, indexing mechanism and balance assembly.	Overhaul the movement; if metal chips or lint are stuck to the magnets, remove with masking tape.
	5) Interference in indexing mechanism.	Check the functions of the indexing mechanism.	Adjust or change index wheel and/or pallet.
	6) Disconnection or poor contact of terminals.	Observe condition of terminals.	Lightly scrape hooked terminals. Connect terminal contacts by tightening screws. Change electronic circuit if leads are damaged.

SYMPTOM	PROBABLE CAUSES	DIAGNOSTIC PROCEDURE	REMEDIAL ACTION
	7) Faulty coil.	Loosen terminal screws of the coil assembly and remove both of the terminal wires (blue and yellow circuit leads). Measure coil resistance with an ohmmeter; crown in setting position. Place the (-) test prod in the screw hole of each terminal of the coil assembly and the (+) test prod on the cell strap screw. See Figure 2.	If resistance is less than 4,000 ohms or more than 6,000 ohms, coil assembly should be changed.
	8) Faulty circuit.	Low balance motion and poor performance when visual examination indicates no mechanical fault or obvious nicks, scratches, or damaged circuit boards.	Replace circuit.
	9) Improper electrical contact or dirt at "make" points of switch.	Inspect action of switch blade and condition of electrical contact points. Electrical continuity of switch can be determined (not required) with a voltmeter, placing (-) test prod on "E" and (+) test prod to ground (see Figure 3). With stem in setting position zero voltage should be indicated.	Adjust switch blade (Figure 4) and/or clean electrical contact spots with deer skin or chamois stick.

CARAVELLE 12 OTC EXPLODED VIEW AND PARTS NAMES

Exploded View of Component Parts (Bridge side)

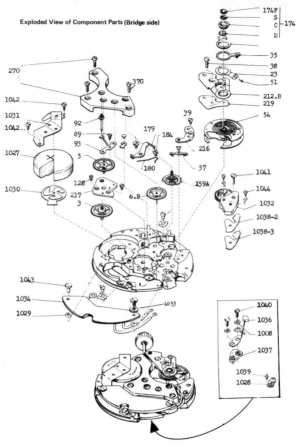

Part No.	Part Name	Part No.	Part Name
3	S.S. center wheel	216	Pallet bridge
5	Third wheel	217	Center wheel bridge
6.B	Fourth wheel	219	Bal. bridge support block
23	Stud holder	1008	Switch insulator (dial side)
35	Regulator	1027	Power cell
37.G	Train wheel bridge screw	1028	Index wheel magnet (dial side)
38	Balance bridge screw	1029	Circuit insulator
39	Pallet bridge screw	1030	Power cell insulator
51	Hairspring stud screw	1031	Power cell strap
54	Balance-complete	1032	Coil assembly
57	Pallet S/S pivots	1033	Circuit screw washer
X59A	Index wheel S/C pivots	1034	Circuit assembly
89	S.S. spring screw	1036	Switch blade (dial side)
92	S.S. pinion	1037	Switch support block
93	S.S. spring	1038-2	Coil shim .05mm
128	Center wheel bridge screw	1038-3	Coil shim .02mm
174C	Upper shock bal. jl. and setting	1039	Index wheel magnet screw (dial side)
174D	Upper shock setting		
174F	Upper cap jewel spring	1040	Switch blade screw (dial side)
174S	Upper cap jewel and setting	1041	Coil assembly screw
179	Stop lever	1042	Power cell strap screw
180	Stop lever spring	1043	Circuit assembly screw
184	Stop lever spring screw	1044	Terminal screw
212.B	Bal. bridge with regulator and stud holder		

REMOVING THE CARAVELLE 12 OTC MOVEMENT FROM WATCH CASE*

A) Place the complete watch in an adjustable waterproof case vice or grasp it securely in hand.

B) Remove the Locking-ring by turning counterclockwise for approximately two (2) turns with an adjustable wrench fitted with suitable attachments.

C) Lift and remove the case back by inserting a screw-driver blade (1.4 mm) between its key and the seat of bezel keyway.

D) Remove the case gasket with tweezers.

E) With the bezel (dial-down) in the case vice or in any well supported manner, place a pointed instrument on the Setting Lever Axle and press firmly; pull the stem and crown straight out.

F) Reposition the case back over the movement, without the Locking-ring, and while holding the back finger-tight, turn watch case over to dial-up position. Carefully lift bezel straight up, leaving movement exposed and resting on case back.

G) Remove the Movement Ring.

H) Place the movement (dial-up) in an adjustable movement holder that will accept its 28 mm or 12½ ligne diameter. Replace stem, by aligning its square with the square in the clutch and push straight in. Firm pressure will cause the set lever to position itself properly in the detent slot of the stem.

*The watch case, component parts and removal procedures referenced in this chapter relate to the styles and design used at the time of introduction. Future creation of new styles and/or case redesign may modify configuration and details in procedures.

MOVEMENT DISASSEMBLING PROCEDURE

The Electrical System

A) With movement dial-up in a movement holder of your choice, pull the crown and stem "out" to setting position. Remove hands; loosen dial screws #47; remove dial with dial insulator attached; hour wheel and cannon pinion. Tighten dial screws to prevent their coming out during subsequent handling.

B) Remove switch blade screws #1040; Two switch insulators #1008, switch blade #1036 and switch support Block #1037.

C) Reposition the movement in movement holder in dial-down position. Loosen (4 turns) power cell strap screws #1042 and turn power cell strap #1031 counterclockwise approximately 50°; remove power cell #1027. The power cell insulator #1030; cell strap screws and cell strap may now be removed.

D) Loosen both terminal screws #1044 that attach the lead wires of the circuit assembly to the coil assembly #1032.

E) Remove coil assembly screw #1041; coil assembly #1032 and coil shims #1038.
NOTE: A different number of coil shims may be used, depending upon the gap between the balance wheel magnets and coils, to center the position of the flat coils.

F) Remove two circuit assembly screws #1043 and the circuit screw washer #1033.

G) Remove the circuit assembly #1034 and circuit insulators #1029.

The Mechanical System

A) After removing the electrical system, place movement in dial-down position in movement holder and push the stem "in" to running position. Remove upper balance cap jewel spring #174.F; balance cap jewel and setting #174.S and spiral spring with balance hole jewel #174.C from the shock-absorber block #174.D.

B) Remove balance bridge screw #38 and balance bridge #212.B with balance assembly attached then remove balance bridge support block #219.

C) Loosen hairspring stud screw #51, disconnect hairspring stud from balance bridge and separate balance assembly #54 from its bridge. Retighten hairspring stud screw #51 to prevent its coming out during subsequent handling.

D) Remove pallet bridge screw #39; pallet bridge #216 and pallet #57.

E) Remove train wheel bridge screws #37G and train wheel bridge.

F) Remove fourth wheel #6B, index wheel #X59A, third wheel #5, and sweep-second pinion #92.

G) Remove center wheel bridge screws #128, and center wheel bridge #217.

H) Remove center wheel #3.
NOTE: The stop lever #179 and spring #180 need not be removed unless damaged.

I) Turn movement to dial-up position, remove lower balance cap jewel spring; balance cap jewel and setting and spiral spring with balance hole jewel from the shock-absorber block.

J) Remove lower index wheel cap jewel spring and cap jewel. The setting mechanism can be left in the lower plate when ultrasonic cleaning equipment is used. If mechanical cleaning equipment is used steps "K" through "N" should be followed.

K) Remove minute wheel bridge screws and minute wheel bridge.

L) Remove minute wheel and setting wheel.

M) Remove set bridge screws, set bridge #28, clutch lever, setting lever, and setting lever axle.

N) Remove stem and clutch wheel.
NOTE: The adjustable, screw-locked, index wheel magnet #1028 is paint-locked at the factory and should not be removed. Cleaning and/or rinsing may remove original paint-lock. However, the index magnet assembly will not move unless its lock screw is loosened. The function "draw" will be affected if the index wheel magnet is moved. Section 4, paragraph "A" describes how to examine and readjust "draw" when necessary.

ASSEMBLING PROCEDURE

THE MECHANICAL SYSTEM

A) Place the lower plate in the movement holder in dial-up position. Assemble the lower complete balance shock assembly, and the lower index wheel jewel assembly. Lubricate both assemblies with Synt-A-Lube (Moebius #OL216) or similar type lubricant.

B) Turn movement over and replace stop lever spring #180 and stop lever #179 if they have been removed. Lubricate the stop lever pivot and actuator lever for stop lever with Synt-Visco-Lube (Moebius #OL219). The actuator lever must be rotated to the maximum clockwise (as it is now viewed) position.

C) Replace center wheel and lubricate upper pivot with Synt-A-Lube.

D) Replace center wheel bridge #217 and its screws #128.
   NOTE: Pressure of the friction spring for sweep-second pinion #93 (attached to the center wheel bridge) should be great enough to prevent forward motion of the sweep-second hand at the moment of shock (on the wrist). Correct pressure will not alter (reduce) the balance motion.

E) Lubricate sweep-second pinion #92 bearings with Synt-A-Lube and replace, followed by third wheel #5, index wheel #X59A, and fourth wheel #6B.

F) Replace the train wheel bridge and its screws #37G.

G) Lubricate train wheel pivots in train bridge and lower plate bushings (7 locations) with Synt-A-Lube. The center wheel arbor should be lubricated and cannon pinion carefully pressed down to properly engage with teeth of minute wheel.
   If setting mechanism and dial train were removed, steps "H" through "L" should be followed. If these parts were left in place, lubricate as indicated in those steps and proceed in reassembly with step "M".

H) Place movement in dial-up position in movement holder; lubricate stem with Synt-Visco-Lube; replace clutch wheel and stem.

I) Replace set lever axle; setting lever and clutch lever; lubricate setting lever and clutch lever with Synt-Visco Lube.

J) Replace set bridge #28 and its screws. Lubricate the pin of the setting lever with Synt-Visco-Lube.

K) Lubricate (sparingly) the minute wheel pivoting post and setting wheel with Synt-Visco-Lube. Replace minute wheel and setting wheel.

L) Replace minute wheel bridge and screws.

M) Place movement in dial-down position in movement holder, replace jeweled pallet #57; pallet bridge #216 and its screw #39.

N) Lubricate contact surfaces of pallet stones and pivots of pallet arbor with Synt-A-Lube.

O) Loosen hairspring stud screw #51 and attach the balance assembly #54 to balance bridge #212.B, then retighten stud screw.

P) Replace balance bridge support block #219.

Q) After pushing the crown and stem "in", replace balance bridge with balance assembly attached and secure the bridge screw #38.

R) Lubricate with Synt-A-Lube and assemble the upper balance shock-absorber parts #174.C and #174.S, and position under cap jewel spring #174.F.

NOTE: It is recommended that the outer coil of the hairspring be adjusted to remain in contact with inside pin of the regulator at any degree or turn of balance motion. Inspect for and adjust to obtain very light contact of hairspring with pin when balance wheel is rotated to maximum distance counterclockwise.

CLEANING

Ultrasonic cleaning equipment is preferred and recommended in cleaning the 12 OTC movement or parts. Partial disassembly of the movement for cleaning is possible. Ultrasonic cavitation actually scrubs all surfaces thoroughly with parts in close proximity; however, inspection and oiling will necessitate further disassembly. Some watchmakers may prefer to disassemble the movement completely and the procedures are outlined in this chapter. Do not use the "plastic lubricant" process with electrical or electronic watches. The following parts *should not* be submerged in watch cleaning solution or subjected to ultrasonic cavitation.

Circuit Assembly #1034	Switch Blade #1036
Power Cell Insulator #1030	Switch Insulators #1008
Coil Assembly #1032	Switch Support Block #1037
Power Cell #1027	Dial Insulator

The negative (-) contact point of the power cell insulator #1030, switch blade #1036, power cell bridge #1031, and power cell #1027 should be wiped clean with a chamois or deerskin stick.

Carefully inspect the balance wheel magnets and the adjustable index wheel magnet after cleaning. Masking tape or Rodico can be used to remove any metal particle which may cling to these permanent magnets. In cleaning the center wheel bridge #217 avoid bending the sweep-second spring #93.

THE ELECTRICAL SYSTEM

A) With the stem and crown pulled "out" in setting position; replace coil assembly #1032 and loosely install coil assembly screw #1041; insert coil shims #1038 and tighten coil assembly screw.

NOTE: The coil should be horizontally centered between balance wheel magnets using suitable shims (space range .05 to .15 mm). The curved (convex) edge of the coil assembly should match the outer curvature of the lower plate when secured by its screw, such "location" will retain previous beat relation.

FIGURE 4

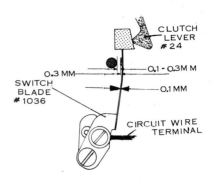

B) Replace circuit insulators #1029; circuit assembly #1034; circuit assembly washer #1033 and screws #1043.

C) Attach the two longest lead wires of circuit to the coil assembly terminals (blue tubed lead wire to inside, the yellow to outside terminal) and tighten screws #1044.

D) Turn movement to dial-up position and replace switch support block #1037; switch blade #1036, position the terminal of the circuit wire as shown in Figure 4, replace the two switch insulators #1008; and two screws #1040.

E) Power cell #1027 voltage should be 1.4 volts or above (using a high resistance voltmeter). It is wise to install a new power cell in every repair, using only the genuine 12 OTC CARAVELLE power cell.

F) Turn movement over to dial-down position and replace cell insulator #1030; power cell #1027; power cell strap #1031 and both screws #1042.

After the above steps ("A" through "F") have been completed, the following should be checked in order to determine condition and functional ability of the movement.

1) Check start and stop action.

2) The balance motion or amplitude should be between 260° and 290° (1 3/8 to 1 5/8 turns) in the flat position. If balance motion is lower than specified recheck power cell voltage and if it is correct (1.4v to 1.6v) the balance assembly should be tested for unnecessary damping.

3) Mechanical interference (damping) of balance motion can be detected through close inspection of parts associated with the balance wheel or through a time measure of the free oscillating balance assembly. Damping tests are made only in the flat position without a power cell installed. Rotate the balance assembly to its maximum point (roller jewel contacting the back or outer surface of pallet lever horn) and then releasing. The index wheel should advance for an interval of ten to fifteen seconds before stopping. If the index wheel stops in less than ten seconds, inspect for and eliminate mechanical interference or damping.

G) Replace hour wheel and dial washer. Loosen dial screws and replace dial with dial insulator attached, tighten screws and affix hands.

ADJUSTMENT OF THE
INDEXING MECHANISM

If the index wheel #X59A or pallet #57 is replaced, it is necessary to check the functions of the indexing system and make adjustments as indicated. After installing the replacement part, proceed in accordance with the following:

A) MAGNETIC DRAW AND DROP. Make certain that the index wheel drops onto and bears against the locking face of the pallet stones. If the pallet lever is not pulled to the banking pins by the index wheel it is necessary to increase the magnetic draw. This is accomplished by moving the index wheel magnet #1028 in the direction of "A" in Figure 5. The correctness of magnetic draw is then determined in draw length, by moving the pallet and observing the distance that the locking corner of the exit pallet stone rides across the leading face, incline "d", of the index wheel tooth. Contact should continue, as the index wheel tooth is being pulled magnetically, until the locking corner of the exit pallet stone has traveled from unlocking to a point between 1/6 and 1/3 of the distance across incline "d". Draw length can be decreased by moving the index wheel magnet in the direction of "B". A similar check can be made on the entry side. See Figure 5.

At the point where contact between the pallet stone and index wheel tooth ceases, the index wheel is held stationary by the index wheel magnet and is in proper position to be advanced by the opposite pallet stone.

NOTE: The adjustable index wheel magnet is correctly positioned at the factory and paint-locked. Unless pallet or index wheel is replaced, this magnet's position rarely requires adjustment. Cleaning or rinsing solutions may remove part or all of the paint-lock; however, the magnet assembly will not move unless its lock screw is loosened.

B) TOTAL ENGAGEMENT. This feature is comparable to total lock (drop-lock plus slide) in a conventional escapement. When the pallet lever is at rest against a banking pin the proper amount of pallet stone engagement is approximately 1/3 of the pallet stone width. See Figures 6 and 7. Before making any changes in pallet stone settings check roller jewel clearance as explained in the next step.

C) ROLLER JEWEL CLEARANCE. The model 12 OTC incorporates a roller jewel that is round in shape; however, clearances are judged and adjusted in the same manner as in a conventional escapement. Due to balance wheel construction, roller

166

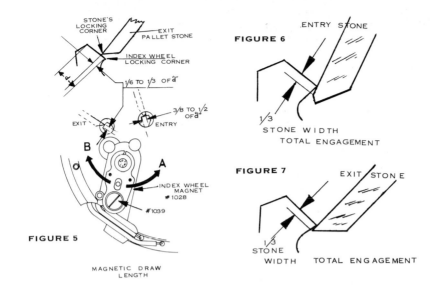

FIGURE 5

MAGNETIC DRAW
LENGTH

FIGURE 6

STONE WIDTH

TOTAL ENGAGEMENT

FIGURE 7

STONE
WIDTH   TOTAL ENGAGEMENT

jewel testing can be most conveniently accomplished through the pallet stone "peep holes" in the lower plate.

By means of the balance wheel move the pallet until drop just occurs on the entry side. Hold the balance wheel in this position, and with a fine probe push against the lift angle of the pallet stone so as to back up the pallet against the roller jewel. Observe the engagement between the pallet stone and the index wheel tooth. Check the exit side similarly. If disengagement occurs on either side it will be necessary to move either one or both of the pallet stones out. If no disengagement occurs but roller jewel clearance appears excessive, bend the banking pins inward to obtain the desired clearance. Excessive roller jewel clearance should be avoided as it will impair balance wheel motion.

D) GUARD PIN SHAKE. This element is judged and adjusted in the same manner as in a conventional escapement.

CASING THE CARAVELLE
12 OTC MOVEMENT

A) With the movement in *setting position* and placed dial-down in a movement holder, use a pointed instrument to press on the setting lever axle and pull stem straight out.

B) Remove the movement from movement holder, affix the movement ring, and place on the case back at dial-up position. Locate bezel over the movement and carefully lower it to touch case back. Turn the case over by temporarily holding the back in place, finger tight. Replace stem by matching its square properly with the clutch and press in firmly.

C) Place a *new* case gasket in the gasket seat of the bezel and position case back to accept locking-ring.
D) Tighten the locking-ring with a Bulova "L" wrench or any other suitable wrench.

CITIZEN X-8 COSMOTRON

While the Caravelle 12 OTC is a restricted calibre of the Citizen Watch company's family of electronic men's watches; yet they have many parts in common. Therefore, the repair and testing of the X-8 series of watches (calibres 0802, 0880, 0840, 0820, 4820, 4840) follow closely to the same procedures as the Caravelle 12 OTC.

Citizen calibre 0802, now discontinued, had a tiny rheostat to regulate balance amplitude. For battery replacements on all X-8 calibres, use the Caravelle 12 OTC energy cell.

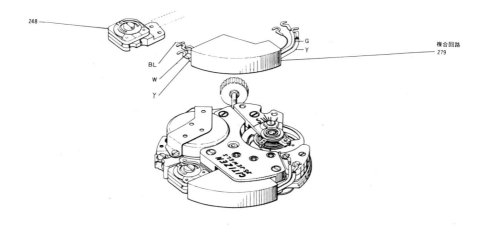

CARAVELLE
(Model 7OT)

FIGURE 1

Figure 1 shows both the dial and movement side of this model. A tiny (5.20mm by 7.80mm) battery supplies 1.5 volts, running it for more than a year.

This model is 7 3/4 lignes round, beats 6 times a second (21,600 times an hour). Pulling the crown outward to the handsetting position acts as a hack mechanism and to disconnect the electrical circuit.

The watch is also self-starting; it does so instantly when the crown is pushed inward. This calibre is also equipped with a device to regulate the amplitude. As with other battery-operated watches, servicing the Caravelle 7OT requires only a multimeter with an internal resistance of 20,000 ohms per volt for measuring DC volts, ohms and microamperes (μA).

Before starting the step-by-step service, it is important that this Caravelle 7OT, like most electronic timepieces, not be put through a demagnetizer. The main plate and balance wheel contain permanent magnets that would be impaired by demagnetization.

Battery Replacement

1) Pull the stem into the setting position. This will insure that the clutch lever's insulated shoe remains under the curved end of the battery connector (1086).

2) Open the case. If the case is a snap-back type, use the Caravelle case opener (7037).
   Because this case back's opening does not extend beyond the bezel, ordinary case openers or knives will not engage it. If this special case opener is not available, the case may be opened by removing the spring bar at the 12 o'clock position where the opening slot is located.
   Select a screwdriver with a blade width of between 2mm and 3mm. Push it against the underside of the lip and twist the screwdriver to pry up the back.
   It's usually best to remove the case lug before inserting the opener for easy removal of the back.

3) With the stem in the hand-setting position, remove the battery strap screw (1083), the battery strap (1056) and the battery (1027).
4) Put in the new battery with the imprinted side up.
5) Reposition the gasket; replace the case back.
6) Push the stem into the running position.

Cleaning and Replacement Hints

Be sure the cleaning and rinsing solutions are free of magnetic particles. To remove these particles, immerse a magnet into the solution; sweep through it and withdraw the magnet.

Do not subject the circuit and coil assembly (1001) to cleaning or rinsing solutions. If cleaning is necessary, use a watchmaker's air blower and a very soft brush.

The lower jewel setting (Rubifix) (122) cannot be disassembled because both hole and cap jewels are friction-fit into the same mounting. The three openings around the edge of this (cap) jewel unit allow the cleaning and rinsing solutions to remove dried oil and permit rinsing and drying. Ultrasonic cleaning is recommended for this model.

If the balance wheel (54) or circuit and coil assembly (1001) are defective, replace these with complete new units.

Replacing Battery Insulator

Remove the old insulator. (If it is the older type, which is one piece and includes the power connector insulator (1087), remove the entire insulator.

If necessary, clean the battery seat in the lower plate (201). Apply a light coat of cement to the battery seat in the lower plate to secure it.

Demagnetizing

Never demagnetize the balance wheel (54) or the lower plate (201). You may demagnetize the other parts though its not necessary.

Lubrication Chart

Part	Lubricant
Balance jewels	Synt-A-Lube, OL 216
Index wheel pivots	Synt-A-Lube, OL 216
Train wheel pivots	Synt-A-Lube, OL 216
Center wheel pivots	Synt-A-Visco Lube, OL 219
Cannon Pinion	Synt-A-Visco Lube, OL 219
Setting mechanism	Synt-A-Visco Lube, OL 219

Disassembling

1) To uncase the movement see step 2 under "Battery Replacement."
2) Remove the battery strap (1056), its screw (1083) and the battery (1027).
3) Loosen the set lever screw (48) and remove the stem (142A).
4) Remove the movement from the case and replace the stem (142A) in the movement. Secure the set lever screw (48).
5) Remove the dial and hands.

NOTE: Dial screws (47) must be completely removed, because they thread into the hollow dial legs. The dial legs are located at the 1:30 and 6:30 positions.

6) Remove the hour wheel.

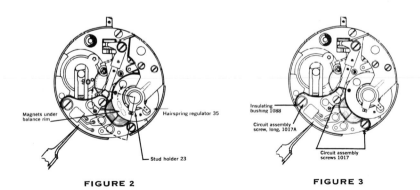

Magnets under balance rim

Hairspring regulator 35

Stud holder 23

FIGURE 2

Insulating bushing 1088

Circuit assembly screw, long, 1017A

Circuit assembly screws 1017

FIGURE 3

The Electrical System

The circuit and coil assembly (1001).

CAUTION: Study all of Step 7 before proceeding to service the electrical system.

7) Move the stud holder (23) clockwise 90°. This moves the balance wheel magnets away and clear of the coil, as shown in Figure 1.
   To prevent damage to the hairspring when moving the stud holder (23), make certain the regulator (35) follows along with the stud holder and does not lag behind it.
8) Remove the large-headed circuit and assembly screws (1017A), as shown in Figure 2.

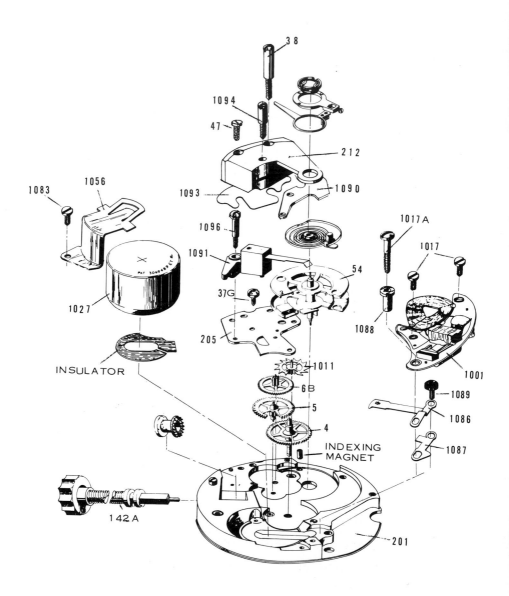

9) Remove the two brass circuit and coil assembly screws (1017A).

10) Remove the circuit assembly (1001) in the following manner: The coil lies between the rims of the balance wheel (54). To avoid damaging this coil, first swing the circuit and coil assembly (1001) out of the way of the balance. When the circuit assembly (1001) is completely free, grasp it by its outer edge and carefully lift it out of the movement.

11) Remove the bushing (1088) that insulates the long circuit assembly screw (1017A) and the power connector (1086). See Figure 2.

Mechanical System

12) Remove the balance bridge (212). Insert a screwdriver in the slot beneath this bridge to pry it up. This minimizes the possibility of disturbing the position of the amplitude regulator (1090), in Figure 3.

13) The balance wheel (54) can be separated from its bridge in the usual manner.

14) Remove the stop lever (1091) and its screw (1096).

15) Remove the cannon pinion (11).

16) Remove the train bridge (205), its screw (37G) and the entire train — the center wheel (4), the third wheel (5), the fourth wheel (6B) and the index wheel (1011).

17) Remove the minute wheel bridge (1092) and the dial train in the conventional manner. Then remove the clutch lever (24) with care so as not to deform it.

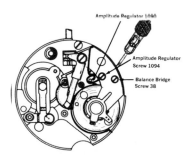

FIGURE 4

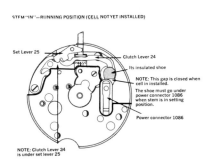

FIGURE 5

Assembly

1) Assemble the setting mechanism. (See the lubrication chart covered earlier.) To replace the clutch lever (24), hold it at its screw end and slide it under the tail of the setting lever (25). See Figure 4.

2) Replace the setting wheel (29) with the bevel side down. Then replace the minute wheel (8), minute wheel bridge (1092) and its screw (1100).
   a) Check the freedom and endshake of all setting wheels.
   b) Check proper functioning of the clutch lever (24).

3) Replacing the train.
   a) Check the index wheel (1011) for cleanliness.
   b) Oil the index wheel jewel setting (1046). See the lubrication chart.
   c) Replace the train in the following sequence: center wheel (4), fourth wheel (6B), the index wheel (1011), the third wheel (5).

4) Replace the train bridge (205) and its screw (37). Check the train wheel endshake. Lubricate the center wheel arbor to prepare for Step 5. Refer to the lubrication chart.

5) Replace the cannon pinion. *Be certain to support the center wheel pinion from the train side to prevent distorting the train bridge.*

6) Check the "rest position" of the index wheel (1011). Turn the train by pushing at the center wheel. Make sure the train always comes to a stop with a tooth of the index wheel centered over the permanent magnet-stud in the lower plate (201).

   Then nudge the wheel half the distance of the space between the teeth. Under the influence of the magnet the wheel should jump to its next position. That is, the tooth of the index wheel becomes positioned over the stud-magnet. If it fails to do so, recheck the train for cleanliness and freedom. If necessary, reclean the parts.

   Repeat the checks covered previously. If the index wheel still does not respond, the stud magnet is defective and you should replace the lower plate (201).

7) Oil and assemble the balance jewels following the instructions covered earlier in the lubrication chart.

8) Examine the balance wheel (54). The four balance magnets and the balance pivots must be free of magnetic particles. To remove foreign particles, use masking tape or Rodico, rolled into a suitable point. Make sure both disks of the balance are "true-in-the-flat."

174

9) Reassemble the balance wheel (54) to its bridge (212).

10) Replace the balance and bridge. Secure the bridge screw. Check the balance wheel endshake. To help adjust endshake, balance bridge shims (1093) are available in .02mm, .03mm and .05mm thicknesses.

Remember in any transistorized balance such as this (with biplane disks with pairs of two magnets and counterpoises facing each other), correct balance endshake is very important. Excessive endshake may cause these magnets and their diametrically opposite counterpoises to touch the stationary coils.

The air gaps between the magnets and the coils must be equal both below and above. See Step 13.

Check the distance between the amplitude regulator (1090) (the small brass lever on the base of the balance bridge) and the upper and lower balance magnets. The amplitude regulator should be approximately centered between the magnets.

If it is not, it may be the result of an unusual condition such as a bent balance disk or the amplitude regulator itself may be bent.

11) Check the coil and circuit assembly (1001) for cleanliness. Make certain the contact surfaces on the underside of the circuit assembly are clean.

If necessary, clean this area with watchmaker's blower and a very soft brush. Clean other metallic parts of this assembly with pithwood.

CAUTION: Cleaning solutions will damage the circuit assembly.

12) Replace the circuit assembly (1001).

   a) Check the position of the balance magnets to make sure they are away from and clear of the coil position. See Figure 1.

   b) Assemble the insulated bushing (1088) to the circuit assembly (1001).

   c) Before installing the circuit assembly, note the coil can be damaged by contact with the rims of the balance wheel assembly.

   First, pick up the circuit assembly. Keep the coil section well away from the balance wheel. Insert the bushing (1088) into the lower plate. See Figure 2. Then cautiously swivel the circuit assembly around the bushing into the lower plate until the coil is positioned between the upper and lower rims of the balance wheel.

d) Replace the two identical circuit assembly screws (1017) — see Figure 2 — but tighten them only after the coil is correctly positioned. Read Step 13 before completing this replacement.

13) Check the position of the coil in relation to the balance magnets. The coil should have a minimum clearance of .05mm on either side. If the clearance is incorrect, remove the balance assembly. Then, using a staking set or a jeweling set, raise or lower the two threaded supports on which the circuit assembly (1001) rests. These supports are friction-fit into the lower plate (201).

To lower, press on the heads of the screws (1017). See Figure 2. To raise, select the correct staking or jeweling pusher and push against these frictioned supports from the dial side.

Make certain these two supports are adjusted equally or the coil will not rest on an even plane.

14) Replace the balance stop lever (1091) and its screw (1096). Check for proper functioning.

Electrical and Functional Check

The multimeter should have an internal resistance of 20,000 ohms per volt for measuring DC volts, ohms and microamperes (μ A).

Needle points on the probes are necessary to prevent their slipping off the contact points and damaging the fine wires of the coil and points to be contacted.

If your meter is not equipped with needle probes, the original test-set leads can be replaced with ones that have threaded collars. These collared ends will accept all types of probes including those with needle points.

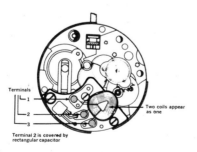

Terminals
1
2
3

Two coils appear as one

Terminal 2 is covered by rectangular capacitor

FIGURE 6

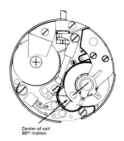

Center of coil 90° motion

FIGURE 7

Checking the Coils

There are actually two coils which appear as one. Refer to Figure 5. To check the coils, set the meter to read ohms. If the meter has more than one setting, use the R10 or the R100 (Ω by 10, or Ω by 100). To test one coil, place the test probes on terminals 1 and 2. (Terminal 2 is covered by a rectangular capacitor. Hold the test probe against the soldered point at the edge of the capacitor.

To test the other coil, place the probes on terminals 1 and 3. If the needle on the meter's dial doesn't move, or if it swings to zero, the coil is defective and you should replace the electronic circuit (1001). (The resistance of each coil, on terminals 1 and 2, or 1 and 3, should be between 2700 and 3300 Ω.)

NOTE: To ascertain the efficiency of the circuitry's power consumption, take a microampere reading with the power cell in the watch and the multimeter set to read microamperes. Place the red (+) probe on the top of the power cell, while the watch is running, and the black (-) probe on the number 2 contact. *(See Figure 5.)*

A reading of 5 μA to 7 μA indicates an efficient and acceptable situation. A reading of more than 7 A indicates mechanical or electronic impediments. The manufacturers claim such a test is not necessary if all the other checkpoints have been covered. It is included here for those who normally follow such a procedure with all their electric watch repairs.

Power Cell Check

Important note: Make sure you use only the genuine Caravelle 7OT power cell (#1027). Do not use substitutes such as hearing-aid batteries. Although their outer appearance is similar, they use a different electrolyte and a different sealing technique. Substitutes may leak corrosive materials and damage the movement. (The manufacturer will not be responsible for any damage caused by the use of substitute materials.)

Set the meter to use the lowest voltage range that will indicate 1.5 volts DC (see Figure 6). Place the black (-) test probe at the center of the gasket-side of the battery. Place the red (+) test probe against the wall of the battery. If the battery reads less than 1.4 volts, replace it. If you use an Accutron Power Cell Tester, follow the instructions provided with that meter but disregard the OK mark on the dial. If the voltage reads less than 1.4 volts, replace the battery.

Balance Motion Check

Check the damping (free movement) of the balance motion should be done with the cell *outside* the movement. To judge the free movement of the balance wheel, measure the time it takes for the balance motion (amplitude) to die down from 315° to 90°.

To check this:

1) Rotate the balance wheel 315° from its rest position (a 3/4 turn or 270°, plus an additional 1/8th turn or 45°).

2) Release the balance and observe how long it takes for the amplitude to drop to 90° (when the two holes of the balance wheel appear to be superimposed over the center of the coil as in Figure 6).

If the time is less than 10 seconds, the motion is faulty. Thoroughly check the movement, re-examine the balance, inspect the parts for cleanliness and test the train for freedom.

Check Shut-Off Switch

Make sure the stem is in. With a pointed tool, depress the spring-like power connector (1086) until its tongue is below the clutch lever's insulated shoe. Then pull the stem out to the setting position. This will align the power connector and shoe correctly.

Install the battery and secure the battery strap and its screw. Push the stem in. Make sure the balance wheel is running.

Check the operation of the shut-off switch (clutch lever 24) by pulling the stem out to the setting position. The balance should stop running. Then lift up the balance wheel stop lever (1091). If the switch (24) is functioning properly the circuit will be open, no current will flow and the balance wheel will not resume running.

Balance Wheel Amplitude

Preparation: Check the beat; if necessary, by means of the stud holder (23).

NOTE: On the timing machine, this type of watch can produce beat lines relatively far apart and still be within acceptable tolerances. On some timing machines, acceptable lines can have as much as a 5mm spread. Generally, the watch is "in beat" when, without power, the two upper and two lower balance magnets are centered over the coil. The amplitude of the balance in each direction should be no more than 280° in the horizontal position and 230° in the vertical or edge positions.

Checking Balance Motion

1) The motion is 280° when the images of the holes in the balance cross and are tangential as shown in Figure 7.

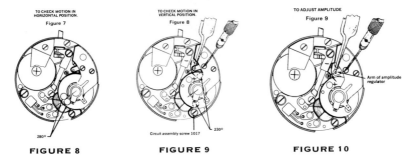

FIGURE 8   FIGURE 9   FIGURE 10

2) At 230°, the image of the hole in the balance seems to stop in line with the circuit assembly screw (1017), and the opposite hole appears to stop partially under the balance bridge as shown in Figure 8.

3) If the balance motion is too great or too low, correct it using the amplitude regulator (1090) as follows:

   a) Loosen screw 1094. Insert a sharp tool into the hole of the amplitude regulator (1090) as shown in Figure 9.

   b) Move the arm of the amplitude regulator *toward* the balance to *increase* the motion, and *away* from the balance wheel to *decrease* the motion.

   c) After the proper motion has been achieved, secure the amplitude regulator by means of its screw. When tightening the screw, hold the amplitude regulator in its chosen position with tweezers in order to prevent shifting.

Adjusting Daily Rate

Check the daily rate on the timing machine. If adjustment is needed, correct the timing with the hairspring regulator. Make certain, while doing this, that the hairspring does not become crimped. Likewise, when moving the beat regulator be sure the hairspring regulator moves along with it.

Replace the hour wheel, washer and dial. Secure dial screws. Replace hands. Remove stem from movement. Replace movement in case. Replace stem. Secure set lever screw. Test stem. Place open-cased movement on timing machine (21,600 VPH) and regulate. Replace case gasket; be sure it is seated properly. Replace case back so that tab is in bezel slot. Press case shut. Test stem again in the "out" and "in" positions.

ESA 9150 and 9154

The ESA 9150 is a transistorized balance watch. It goes under various names such as Wittnauer, Wyler, Zodiac.

ESA 9154 is the same basic movement but has a faster vibration count of 28,800. The differences and servicing hints on this are on page 199.

Like most transistorized balances, the movement of the magnets on these balances over stationary coils induces a current which "triggers" the transistor, allowing the battery current to flow into the impulsing coil to impel the balance or to attract its magnets. Thus no physical contact is required to energize an electrical impulse. This eliminates one of the problems in "make-and-break" contacts of electrical watches.

While the illustrations shown in this chapter have a Wittnauer label, remember that the exact movement is used with many other company name-brands.

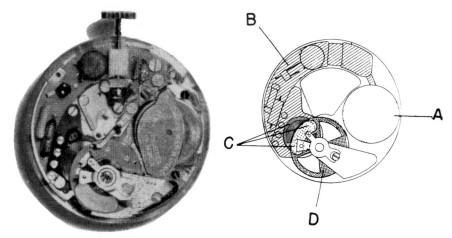

Figure 1: The movement of the Wittnauer Electronic is 28mm (12½ lignes) wide.
Figure 2: A small dry cell (A) powers the watch, supplying a uniform voltage over a long period. The electronic circuit (B) doses the current to the electrodynamic transducer (C), which maintains the oscillations of the balance (D).

A, Figure 2, is a W12NM Mallory battery which can maintain a uniform voltage over a long period. This helps to give the motor-balance its uniform arcs and its isochronism. The electrical current supplied by this cell is dosed by the electronic circuit, B. This contains a planar-type silicon transistor.

The electronic circuit produces current impulses, which are transmitted to an electrodynamic transducer, C. This maintains the oscillations of the balance, D. The balance is both the regulating organ and the motor of the watch. The oscillations of the balance are indexed by a jeweled lever clickwork.

Figure 1 is a photograph of the movement, which is 28mm or 12 1/2 lignes in diameter. The overall thickness is 5.50mm. A train of traditional wheels transmits this motion to the hands and the calendar work.

Coil/Magnet Operation

The operation of this electronic watch is based on the stationary coils, which are straddled by four permanent magnets, two each mounted on balance discs. Two tiny flat magnets are mounted below the level of these coils, and two are mounted on a disc above the coils, as shown in Figure 3A. The stationary coils are disc-shaped, and while appearing as a single unit, are actually two, one atop the other. One is the triggering coil, the other is the impulsing coil. The magnets do not touch the coils, but barely clear them during their oscillations.

When a magnet passes over or near a coil, it induces a current in it. When the balance is moved, as when being started, the magnets passing over the coils induce a current in the triggering coil. This current, though tiny, is sufficient, and is sent through the transistor, where it triggers a release of the energy locked in the cell. This energy, in turn, surging through the impulsing coil, causes a strong electromagnetic impulse on the balance and makes it oscillate.

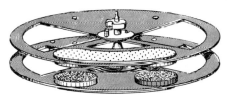

Figure 3: Balance with four opposing disc-magnets, bottom view.

Efficient Balance Operation

The balance is self-starting and at a normal amplitude receives only one driving impulse per oscillation, making for better performance from a chronomatic viewpoint. Additional capacitors and resistors refine the circuitry to maximum efficiency and operation. A detailed description of a similar system appears in Figures 106 and 107, page 86.

The balance, as shown in Figures 3 and 3A, contains two parallel discs with two sets of permanent magnets, comprising part of a magnetic circuit. These discs are contained within kidney-shaped pieces, which serve as shunts. Diametrically opposite these shunts are eccentric weights, which are positioned to affect the poise. Figure 3A shows the balance as viewed from the bottom. Notice the four opposing disc-magnets with their connecting shunts.

The balance contains a roller, roller jewel and safety roller. These do not receive an impulse as in mainspring-driven watches, but instead are the means of imparting an indexing action through a jeweled lever. The lever appears much like that in mainspring watches, except that the jewels' lifting faces are slanted in the opposite direction. When the jeweled lever is moved back and forth by the balance's roller, these slanted lever jewels, working into the specially designed click wheel (escape wheel) teeth cause the click wheel to be indexed, one tooth at a time. In turn, this wheel moves the remainder of the train.

No Checking Necessary

Because the fork's horns and guard finger are precisely ground, no checking of their proper functions is necessary. Proper guard finger clearance and horn clearance can be taken for granted. A tiny magnet situated just behind the guard finger assures the fork's proper banking and clearance by the guard finger of the safety roller when the roller is out of the fork slot and horns.

The hand setting also serves as a hack mechanism and comprises a balance stop. When the stem is pulled out to the setting position, a lever stops the balance near the height of its arc, when the hairspring is tensed. This enables the second hand to be set to the exact second. The stop lever operates a switch at the same time, cutting the current supply from the cell when the watch is not in use. When the stem is pushed back, the balance is released so that, in its tensed position, it becomes self starting.

The calendar mechanism is of the semi-instantaneous type. It does not start to operate until 11:30 P.M. The power required to jump the date is so small (by special design) that there is no perceptible difference in the balance amplitude during this period. Furthermore, less than one revolution of the crown is needed to affect a date correction.

The battery consumption by the electronic system is so small that running time for over a year on one cell is assured. When entirely discharged, the cell can be replaced by a watchmaker in a very short while, as will be shown later. The battery voltage across the terminals of this cell is very stable. Regulation can be affected to a very close limit. Average daily variations are claimed to be less than three seconds.

Figure 4 shows the movement side of the watch, together with the proper nomenclature and official parts number designations.

In the following instructions for repair and servicing, the traditional operations familiar to the watchmaker are merely enumerated. Only special operations are described in detail.

Almost all watchmakers now possess an ohm-voltmeter. The only other special tool required to service this watch is a non-magnetic tweezer. Special caution, however, should be given to the watchmaker: the watch *must* be serviced in the exact sequence given here. Again, it is strongly advised that a stainless steel, non-magnetic tweezer be used to service this watch.

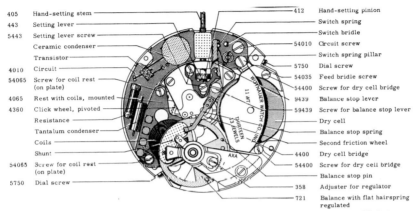

405	Hand-setting stem		412	Hand-setting pinion
443	Setting lever			Switch spring
5443	Setting lever screw			Switch bridle
	Ceramic condenser		54010	Circuit screw
	Transistor			Switch spring pillar
4010	Circuit		5750	Dial screw
54065	Screw for coil rest (on plate)		54035	Feed bridle screw
			54400	Screw for dry cell bridge
4065	Rest with coils, mounted		9439	Balance stop lever
4360	Click wheel, pivoted		59439	Screw for balance stop lever
	Resistance			Dry cell
	Tantalum condenser			Balance stop spring
	Coils			Second friction wheel
	Shunt		4400	Dry cell bridge
54065	Screw for coil rest (on plate)		54400	Screw for dry cell bridge
				Balance stop pin
5750	Dial screw		358	Adjuster for regulator
			721	Balance with flat hairspring regulated

Figure 4: Movement side of the watch, with proper nomenclature and official parts number designations.

Disassembling

Each operation will bear an identifying number to make location of a particular step easier should reference to it be required. The cases for these watches are, for the most part, the one-piece type with snap-stem and movement removed through the crystal side.

First, pull off the snap stem, being careful not to dent or knick the case pipe. Next, with the crystal lifter, remove the crystal. Turning the case over, dial side down, will cause the movement to drop out.

1.1 Removing the Case

Should other than the one-piece case be encountered with this movement, open the case back. Then, loosen the two setting lever screws, 5443, Figure 4. Remove the setting lever, 443, hand setting stem, 405, and hand setting pinion, 412 (there is no clutch wheel).

Take the movement out of the case, remove the hands, loosen the two dial screws, 5750, and remove the dial and hour wheel, 255. Do not attempt to lift off the cannon pinion, as this will only separate it from its frictioned driving wheel below.

1.2 Disassembling, Bridge Side

Loosen the two bridge screws, 54400, of the dry cell bridge and remove the dry cell. Be careful: grasping the cell with the tweezer at its opposite terminals will short it. Loosen the feed bridle screw, 54035 (Figure 4), and remove the feed bridle, 4035, shown separately in Figure 5. Loosen screw 59439 of the balance stop lever and remove the lever, 9439. Loosen the circuit screw, 54010, and the two screws, 54065, of the coil rest (on the plate.)

Figure 5: Detail of the feed bridle (4035) and feed bridle screw (54035). In the disassembling process (bridge side) loosen the screw and remove the feed bridle.

Removing Circuit Unit (Figure 6)

With the right thumb, turn the balance (1) until the stud screw is midway between both balance arms. Hold the balance in this position. With the left thumb, turn the circuit (2) pivoted at (3) until the coil rest is completely free of the balance. Do not use tools for this operation — you may scratch and ruin the coils or the circuit. Release the balance, then, remove the circuit, 4010, Figure 4, and the clear plastic insulator, 4015, shown in Figure 7. Again, do not touch the coils with tweezers. Rather, grasp the plastic plate unit to avoid severing a coil wire. Remove the shock absorber system from the balance bridge. Remove the balance bridge and balance.

Remove the pallet bridge and pallet (click-lever). Loosen the two train bridge screws and carefully loosen the train bridge. Turn the movement over, together with the movement holder (ordinary movement holders will do) and tap the unit to cause the train bridge and the three wheels to drop out. The fourth wheel and click wheel, 4360, sometimes remain attached to the train bridge owing to the pressure of their tension springs, which rest against grooved nylon discs attached to the arbors of the fourth and click wheels. Separate them with care to avoid bending the springs. Leave the mounted double friction (tension) spring, 472, Figure 8, screwed to the underside of the train bridge.

184

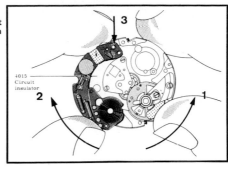

Figure 6: Remove the circuit unit with fingers only — tools may scratch and ruin the coils or the circuit.

4015
Circuit
insulator

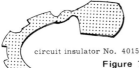

circuit insulator No. 4015

Figure 7: When removing the clear plastic insulator, do not touch the coils with tweezers. Grasp the plastic plate unit to avoid severing a coil wire. 472- DOUBLE FRICTION SPRING

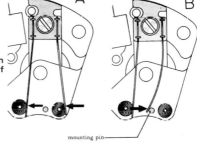

A

B

Figure 8: Leave the mounted double friction (tension) spring screwed to the underside of the train bridge.

mounting pin

1.3 Disassembling, Dial Side

Turn the dial train until the disengaging finger of the date-indicator driving wheel, 2556/1, can be seen. This is the position shown in Figure 9. It would be impossible to remove the minute wheel, 260, if the disengaging finger were above the driving finger of the minute work.

Loosen the two screws, 5462, of the minute wheel bridge and remove the bridge. Remove the minute wheel, 260, and the pivoted setting wheel, 450.

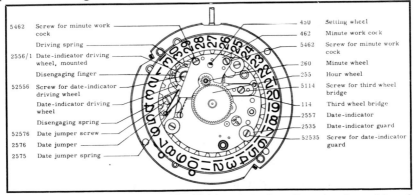

5462	Screw for minute work cock		450	Setting wheel
2556/1	Driving spring		462	Minute work cock
	Date-indicator driving wheel, mounted		5462	Screw for minute work cock
	Disengaging finger		260	Minute wheel
52556	Screw for date-indicator driving wheel		255	Hour wheel
	Date-indicator driving wheel		5114	Screw for third wheel bridge
	Disengaging spring		114	Third wheel bridge
52576	Date jumper screw		2557	Date-indicator
2576	Date jumper		2535	Date-indicator guard
2575	Date jumper spring		52535	Screw for date-indicator guard

Figure 9: The dial side is shown with official parts numbers. Note that the position of the disengaging finger of the date-indicator driving wheel (2556/1) permits the minute wheel to be removed.

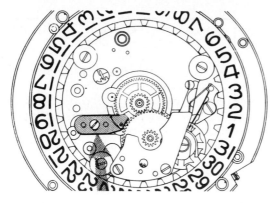

Figure 10: To remove the third wheel (114), remove the screw (5114) and turn the movement over, pushing the bridge outward, at arrow.

The next part to be removed is the third wheel, 114, Figures 9 and 10. This is best done by removing the screw, 5114, and then turning the movement over, pushing the bridge (at arrow, Figure 10) outward. If attempts to remove the cannon pinion are made before this bridge is removed, the cannon pinion will become separated from its frictioned driving wheel.

After the bridge is removed, remove the cannon pinion and its attached driving wheel, 242. Remove the date jumper spring, 2575, and date jumper screw, 52576, and the date jumper, 2576. Disassemble the three date-indicator guards, 2535, and their screws, 52535, Figure 9. Loosen the screw of the date-indicator driving wheel and remove this wheel, 2556/1. Disassemble the shock absorber system of the plate.

2.1 With the strict exception of the balance, all parts may be demagnetized without risk or danger.

2.2 Cleaning

The electronic circuit and the mounted coil-rest are the only parts that should NOT be cleaned. All others, including the date-indicator, 2557, should be cleaned in the usual way. If ultrasonic cleaning is used, it is advisable afterwards to coat the click wheel, 4360, Figure 4, and its click lever (pallet) 4330 (not shown) with "Aretol," a commercially available chemical used to coat parts to prevent oil from spreading.

3. Assembling

3.1 Calendar Mechanism (Figure 9)

The calendar mechanism has two unique features. Date changing is free from any extra strain on the power source, and corrections are made without too much turning of the hands.

Ordinarily, when the date approaches a change, an inordinate strain is placed on the watch's power as the date indicating driving wheel's finger pushes an internal tooth of the indicator (disc-dial). This, in turn, must push aside a spring-loaded date jumper and

186

"climb over" its beak, so that a new date can be indexed and jump into place. In this watch these steps are practically eliminated. The process (3.6.1) will be explained later.

3.1.1 Fit date-indicator driving wheel, 2556/1, and secure its screw tightly. After fitting, its endshake should be .03mm.

In all calendar trains, parts fitted must move freely. If they bind, they will put a strain on the power source. To make certain that this wheel turns freely, direct a jet of air from a blower diagonally across the wheel's edge. The wheel should turn freely.

3.1.2 Place the date-indicator, 2557, in position and secure it by means of the three small disc-guards, 2535, and their screws. This disc-indicator, too, must turn when a jet of air is directed from a bench blower at its internal teeth.

3.1.3 Fit the date jumper, 2576, and tightly secure its screw. Endshake here must be .03mm.

Dial Train Assembly

3.2.1 Lubricate with horological grease the friction between the cannon pinion and its driving wheel at its three clutch points. If these two parts should become separated, they can be snapped back together by placing the cannon pinion downward in a staking block. The driving wheel can then be snapped onto the rear of the cannon pinion. Test the clutch action between these two and adjust if necessary. After lubrication, replace this unit, 242, in position. Next, fit the third wheel bridge, 114, and secure it tightly. Use the blower's jet again to test if the wheel, 242, turns freely. The third wheel bridge tip also acts as a capguard for the cannon pinion driving wheel, 242. If parts 242 and 114 are not assembled in the sequence explained in 3.2.1, the cannon pinion and its driving wheel will separate.

3.2.2 After greasing its two pivots, place the setting wheel, 450, in position.

3.2.3 See Figure 11. Grease the hole of the driving finger of the minute wheel, 260, as well as its edge (lightly). **The tiny bead-headed arrows indicate lubrication points on all figures.**

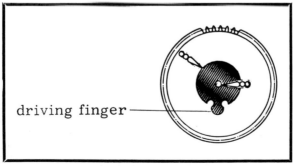

driving finger

Figure 11: The hole and edge of the driving finger of the minute wheel should be greased. Bead-headed arrows indicate lubrication points in all figures.

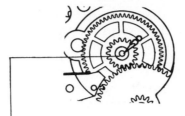

2̶4̶2 Cannon pinion with driving
wheel

Figure 12: A drop of fine oil should be applied in the hole of the center pipe (see section 3.2.9, below).

3.2.4 Turn the date-indicator driving wheel, 2556/1, until its disengaging finger points towards the outside of the plate, as in Figure 9. Fit the minute wheel work, using the peephole to make sure that its driving finger is engaged between two teeth of the driving wheel.

3.2.5 Fit the minute wheel cap, 462, and secure it firmly. Endshake should be .03mm.

3.2.6 Check the entire dial train up to this point for ease of action. Direct a jet of air at the cannon pinion's driving wheel. This should turn these wheels slightly.

3.2.7 Place the date jumper spring, 2575, in position, checking its tension according to the following, shown in Figure 13: the active end of the spring should point towards the tip of the date jumper when the date jumper is resting against and between the internal teeth of the date-indicator, 2557. It will do this if the spring is spread correctly for proper tension. Then nudge the end of this spring behind the jumper pin, as in Figure 9.

3.2.8 Reassemble the shock absorber system of the plate.

3.2.9 Apply a drop of fine oil in the hole of the center pipe, as shown in Figure 12.

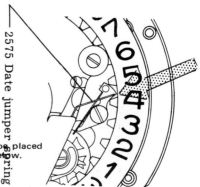

2575 Date jumper spring

Figure 13: The date jumper spring should be placed in position and checked according to 3.2.7, below.

3.3 Train, Click Lever and Balance

3.3.1 Check the tension of the double friction spring, 472, as shown in Figure 8. The straight sides of the two wires should be tangent to the jewels of the sweep second and click wheels, respectively. This check is easily made with a pivot loupe. Also, check that both springs are parallel to the under surface of the bridge. Correct, if necessary.

3.3.2 As shown in Figure 9, place the "click" arm of the double friction spring behind the grooved mounting pin. **Proceed with caution to avoid damaging the working end of this spring.**

3.3.3 Place in position, in this order: the sweep second wheel, the third wheel, the click wheel and the train bridge prepared according to 3.3.2. Place the bridge over the wheels so that their pivots are not yet fully in their jewel holes. Do not yet secure the bridge. Viewed from the front, the tips of the tension springs of 472 will now be seen.

3:3.4 With a fine oiler, nudge the fourth wheel's spring into the groove of the nylon disc mounted on the fourth wheel arbor. Next, secure the pivots in their jewels and secure the bridge screws tightly. Finally, push the spring which you locked behind the mounting pin off this pin. It will drop by itself into the nylon groove of the click wheel.

3.3.5 Check the endshake of these three wheels (tolerance should be 0.02-0.04mm).

3.3.6 The banking magnet of the (click) lever is fixed in the stud of the guard finger. Fine particles of metal collected in the cleaning bath may attach themselves to the extremities of this part. These can be removed easily by pushing the lever fork into a clean piece of pithwood. Place the click lever and its bridge in position. Correct endshake is .02mm.

3.3.7 Lubricate and reassemble the balance bridge shock absorber system. Use adhesive tape to remove metallic particles that may have been attracted magnetically to the balance. The balance pivots can be cleaned with pithwood.

Fit the balance and bridge into position and adjust the hairspring. Balance endshake is .02mm. Check the relative heights of the fork and the roller. There is a special view-way channel in the movement's edge for just this purpose. The horns of the fork should be level with the lower third of the roller jewel (impulse pin).

Check the movement for regular beat on the timing machine. Although the watch is not running on its own, it will give a recording on the machine if the balance is impulsed by a judicious movement with the finger or a soft brush. For the correct beat position, center the balance magnets in relation to the coil, as in Figure 4.

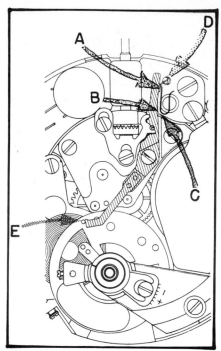

Figure 14: Check height of the balance stop (E) as described in 3.5.5.

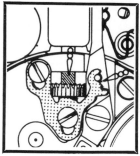

Figure 15: Arrows indicate greasing (3.5.3).

3.4 Fitting the Circuit

3.4.1 Fit the insulator, 4015, Figure 7. Place the circuit unit in position, as shown in Figure 6, with its pivotal swing point at (3). Move the balance away with the thumb of the right hand, as in (1) and keep it in that position. With the circuit unit pivoted at (3), turn the circuit in the opposite direction of the arrow (2), until it is in its correct position in the movement. Insert and tighten the two 54065 screws; first the outer screw of the coil rest, then the inner one. Then, insert and tighten the circuit screw, 54010, which has a larger head but shorter thread than the two 54065 screws. Be careful not to interchange these screws.

3.4.2 Secure the feed bridle screw, 54035, and the feed bridle, Figure 5, centering the three bent-up claws in relation to the dry cell recess.

3.5 Hand-Setting Mechanism

3.5.1 Lightly grease the shoulder screw, 59439, of the balance stop lever. Fit the stop lever, 9439, as shown in Figure 14. The switch spring, D, Figure 14, should push the stop lever against the nylon block of the stem.

3.5.2 Place the hand-setting pinion, 412, in position. Then, grease the hand-setting stem, 405, and insert it by twisting it lightly into the hand-setting pinion.

190

3.5.3 Lightly grease the shoulders of the two setting-lever screws, 5443. Fit the set lever, 443, shown shaded in Figure 15. Secure its screws tightly. If necessary, move the stop lever aside to facilitate its positioning. Grease the functional points of the setting lever and stop lever at the spots shown in Figure 15.

3.5.4 The switch spring is insulated from the stop lever by a ruby-type cap jewel protruding from the side of the stop lever into which it is set (see A, Figure 14). The spring must not touch either the body of the stop lever or the train bridge at the points indicated at A, B or C.

When the spring is pulled out, however, the switch spring should be pushed by the lever so that it presses on the switch bridle at the end of its movement, where an upright pin emerges through the plate (at D). This opens the circuit, avoiding any drain on the dry cell.

3.5.5 Check the height of the balance stop pin, E, Figure 14. The end of the stop spring should not come more than halfway down the pin. This insures sufficient clearance between the stop spring tip and the shunt on the balance when the hand-setting stem is pushed in and the balance oscillates.

3.6 Operation of Calendar When Driven by Movement

3.6.1 The driving finger, solid with the minute wheel, pushes the date-indicator driving wheel one tooth forward every three hours. This wheel is shown in Figure 9, part 2556/1. It is in the form of an eight-toothed Maltese cross. About a half hour before the date changes, the disengaging finger fitted to the driving wheel presses on the disengaging spring, which is solid with the jumper (A). See Figure 16. At that moment, the driving spring is not yet in contact with the indicator (ring dial) tooth (B).

When the driving spring presses on the indicator tooth at 3 (Figure 17), the disengaging finger on the driving wheel has lifted the jumper (D). This releases the indicator, easing the pressure on the calendar dial and time train. Part 2576 thus moves out of the way. From that moment, the driving spring pushes the indicator tooth. At indicated midnight, the disengaging finger releases the jumper, which then drops between the two following teeth of the indicator, positioning the new date.

Compare Figures 16 and 17. Notice how this action is accomplished by the jumper spring, which at times acts as a modified chronometer detent.

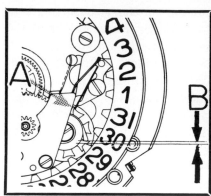

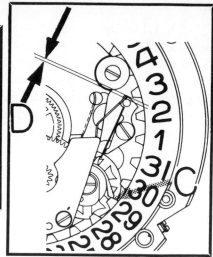

Figure 16: Operation of the calendar when driven by the movement, as explained in 3.6.1.

Figure 17: Pressure on the calendar dial is eased during the date change (3.6.1).

Operation of Calendar When Moved by Hand

3.6.2 The indicator has just changed the date at midnight. To change the date again, it is necessary to move the hands back only about 40 minutes and then to move them forward again as far as midnight. In this case, the mechanism does not operate as in 3.6.1.

When the hands are turned backwards, the disengaging finger meets the disengaging spring detent (which is integral with the jumper). This reinforces the action of the jumper spring, 2575, holding the date indicator motionless (Figure 18 at A).

This support is sufficient to enable the driving spring to move back in front of another tooth (B). Another forward movement of the driving spring causes the jumper to slide on the next tooth.

3.6.3 Lubricating Calendar Mechanism

Lightly grease the three date-indicator guards, 2535, shown shaded in Figure 18 at C. Bring the date-indicator driving wheel, 2556/1, to the position shown in Figure 9. Using a pair of tweezers, turn the indicator until the beak of the jumper comes to rest on top of a tooth. Grease the two sides of the beak as shown in Figure 19 (bead-headed arrows). Repeat the operation at each third turn of the indicator. Grease the functional points of the jumper and the jumper pin at the points indicated by the oiling pointers.

3.6.4 Adjusting the Calendar Mechanism

3.6.4.1 Make certain that during the entire period of the operations described under 3.6.1 and 3.6.3 the disengaging finger passes neither below nor in front of the disengaging spring, which is soldered to the jumper.

If necessary, correct by milling the shoulder screw, 52576, to reduce the jumper's endshake. This can be done on the lathe or with a rose cutter, similar to undercutting a balance screw, but, of course, using a fuller cutter.

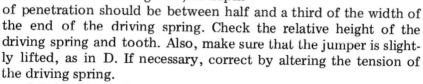

Figure 18: The date changing mechanism does not operate as in 3.6.1 during manual changing (3.6.2).

3.6.4.2 Place the movement's calendar mechanism in the position shown in Figure 17. When the driving spring comes into contact with the indicator tooth according to C, its depth of penetration should be between half and a third of the width of the end of the driving spring. Check the relative height of the driving spring and tooth. Also, make sure that the jumper is slightly lifted, as in D. If necessary, correct by altering the tension of the driving spring.

3.6.4.3 Place the movement in position shown in Figure 9. Lifting the date indicator driving wheel, make sure that the driving spring cannot foul the minute wheel cap, 462. If necessary, correct by milling the shoulder screw, 52556, to reduce the endshake of the driving wheel.

3.6.4.4 To make absolutely certain that the calendar mechanism is operating perfectly, advance the rapid date setting mechanism as indicated in 3.6.2 for a complete revolution of the date indicator, 2557.

3.7 General Lubrication

3.7.1 Lubrication, dial side.
Oil the shock jewels.
Lubricate the click wheel bearings.
Lubricate the third wheel bearings.
Lubricate the bridge side. Oil the shock absorber jewels, the click wheel bearing, fourth wheel bearings, third wheel bearings.

In oiling the click wheel, oil about 12 of the 30 teeth, applying oil at intervals of about three teeth around the whole wheel. This operation can be done either on the bridge side between the train bridge and the coil rest at the points shown at 4360, Figure 4, or on the dial side through the peephole over its edge.

3.8 Checking Balance Freedom (Damping)

Damping consists of measuring the time that elapses between the moment when the balance is released from the end of its swing with the hairspring fully extended and the moment when the balance motion is so small that it fails to index the click wheel.

For a freshly cleaned and oiled movement with its double friction spring and wheels correctly adjusted, a satisfactory period should be between 22 and 29 seconds. If the time measured is less than 20 seconds and the watch has been in service for over two years, a cleaning would be indicated.

3.9 Fitting the Dry Cell

Measure the voltage of the dry cell. It should be 1.35V, although a fresh cell may be as high as 1.4V.

Clean the cell carefully with a clean dry cloth, and fit it into its recess with the + side up. Fit the bridge and secure the screws tightly.

3.10 Checking the Switch

Pull out the hand setting stem, thus locking the balance. Lift the stop spring at E, Figure 14. The balance should be freed, but will gradually come to a stop. If it continues to run, the switch bridle is not touching the switch spring (B, Figure 14). Correct according to 3.5.4.

3.11 Checking the Amplitude

When the movement is in good condition and is fitted with a dry cell of 1.35V, the balance amplitude should have an upper limit, Dial Down (DD) of 270°. This limit is reached when the stop pin of the balance is above the edge of the coils as shown in Figure 19. The lower limit in the Stem Down (PD) position is 220°. In this position, the stop pin is on a line extending from the upper edge of the stud-lug of the balance bridge.

Limit Amplitudes

If the value of the amplitude is outside one or the other limits, check the damping of the balance according to 3.8. If the damping is correct, the fault will be found in the electronic system. This will be discussed later.

3.12 Fitting Dial and Hands

Place the hour wheel in position and fit the dial and hands. The hands must be set to work correctly with the calendar. If the case is other than a one-piece type, remove the setting lever, 443, and the stem. Fit the movement into the case. Replace the stem

194

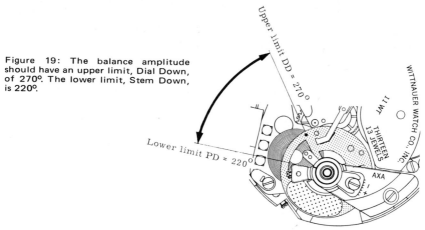

Figure 19: The balance amplitude should have an upper limit, Dial Down, of 270°. The lower limit, Stem Down, is 220°.

and setting lever, and then fix the movement in position. If the case is a one-piece type, the stem and set lever need not be removed to replace the movement in its case. Before closing the case, adjust the daily rate.

3.13 Adjustment of Daily Rate

The balance vibrates a 21,600 (VPH). Set the timing machine accordingly. Note the recorded rate in the PL, PU, PD, DD and DU positions. Calculate the average daily rate between 0 and +5 seconds.

3.14 Final Checking

Having closed the case, test the working of the balance stop system. Check the calendar by advancing the rapid date change mechanism in the DD position on a complete revolution of the indicator (disc-dial). Set the watch to time.

A troubleshooting chart is provided to enable any watchmaker to diagnose the trouble quickly and accurately. Watchmakers should refer to this chart before going any further.

4.3 Balance Damping Data

Measure the damping of the balance according to 3.8. From the value obtained, it is possible to infer one of the following:

4.3.1 When it is under 20 seconds, a complete overhaul is necessary and a new dry cell must be fitted. If the watch has already been overhauled, the fault may be either bad cleaning, incorrect adjustment of the double friction spring, 472, or slightly insufficient endshake.

4.3.2 When the damping is between 22 and 29 seconds, this is considered satisfactory.

4.3.3 When the damping is over 30 seconds, you are most likely measuring the damping without having the circuit part 4010 in position. Replace the circuit in order to conduct the damping test properly.

Electronic Stoppage

4.4.1 Checking the switch spring. Make sure that the switch spring is not causing a short circuit, according to 3.5.4 and Figure 14. This visual check can be completed by measuring the resistance with an ohmmeter (see Figure 20). With the stem pushed in, touch the positive probe of the instrument to the plate or one of the bridges and the negative probe to the switch spring pillar as shown. The resistance value should be infinite. If this is not the case, straighten the spring to eliminate the short circuit.

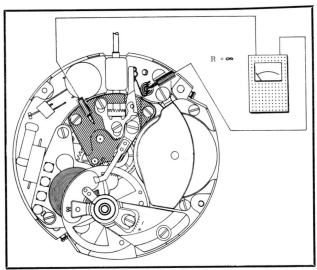

Figure 20: An ohmmeter is used to check that the switch spring is not causing a short circuit. The resistance value should be infinite.

TROUBLESHOOTING CHART

TROUBLE	CORRECTIONS
The Balance is Stopped:	
If it has stopped in the rest position.	Test the dry cell (4.1).
Dry cell causes watch to run.	Check amplitude (3.11). Remove dry cell and measure damping (3.8, 4.3.1, 4.3.3).
Balance doesn't swing freely without dry cell.	Check mechanical causes (4.2.1). Then fit new cell.
Is switch spring in order? (4.4.1)	Straighten spring, then fit new cell.
Balance is still stopped.	Remove coils (4.4.2). Replace mounted coil rest, then fit new cell.
Balance is still stopped.	Faulty circuit. Replace and fit new cell.
Train is stopped.	Check 4.4.2 and repair. Same used cell may be employed.
Amplitude (3.11) has poor motion.	Remove dry cell. Check damping (3.8). If damping is correct, then cell is useless. Replace with new cell and adjust (3.13). Watch may need an overhauling (4.3.1).
Overmotion (rebanking, knocking).	Defective circuit. Replace.
Watch loses greatly when worn.	Double friction spring has insufficient tension. Adjust (3.3.1).
4.1 Discharged Dry Cell.	Measure the voltage of the dry cell in its normal working position: connect the voltmeter terminals to the plate (+) and to the feed bridle screw, 54035 (Figure 5), respectively. If the voltage is below 1.25V, the cell is discharged. Fit a working cell (one which has already been used but which still has a voltage of at least 1.25V) in order to proceed with the examination.
4.2 Mechanical Stoppage. 4.2.1 The balance doesn't swing freely. Possible causes:	
The balance stop spring is pressing on the balance.	Adjust according to 3.5.5.
Insufficient endshake of balance or lever (click).	Adjust endshake to .02mm.
The height of the (lever) fork is too great in relation to the roller.	Adjust according to 3.3.7.
The balance magnets foul the rest with coils.	Lock the four screws fixing the coil to the circuit as well as the screws fixing the circuit to the plate.
4.2.2 The balance swings freely but the train fails to move.	The fault is stoppage either of the hands, the train wheels, the dial train or calendar. Check all the wheels and make certain they turn freely.

4.4.2 Checking the Coils

The coils are mentioned in the plural, but it must be recalled that while there are two coils, these are combined as one unit. To check the coils (only), loosen and remove the four screws, which fix the coil unit to the circuit. Remove the coil unit, which should now appear as in Figure 21 A, B, and C. Check the ohmic resistance between the four coil terminals to ascertain whether the coils are in order or are defective. Proceed as follows:

Figure 21 A: If the resistance is about 1.4k ohms, the first coil is in order. If the resistance is infinite or R = 0, the first coil is defective.

Figure 21 B: If the resistance is about 3.5k ohms, the second coil is in order. If the resistance is infinite or R = 0, the second coil is defective.

Figure 21 C: If the resistance is infinite, the coils are in order. If the resistance has any other value, the coils are defective.

If either of the coils is defective, replace the mounted coil assembly.

FIGURE 21

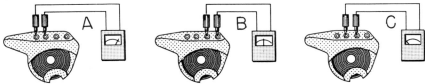

Figure 21: The three positions for checking the resistance of the coils are shown. See 4.4.2 on previous page.

FIGURE 22

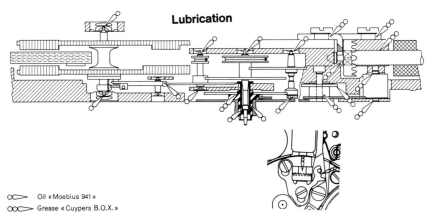

Oil «Moebius 941»
Grease «Cuypers B.O.X.»

ESA 9154
(Dynatron)

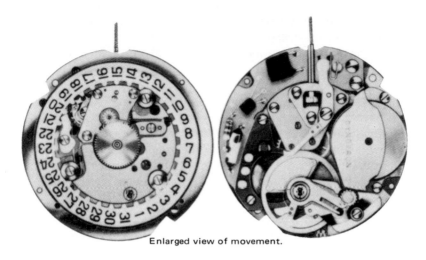

Enlarged view of movement.

Electronic movement with sprung balance, sweep second, calendar mechanism sunk into the plate for showing the date through an aperture in the dial, balance-stop device. 28,800 vibrations per hour.

ESA 9154 is virtually the same as 9150 but has a faster vibration count of 28,800 per hour or eight times a second. Figure 1 shows the calendar side and Figure 2 the movement side. This movement is used by Hamilton, Elgin, Tissot and Girard Perregeaux as well as others.

To service this watch, refer to the previous chapter where noted in the following instructions and will be noted where no change from the 9150 calibre has taken place. The exceptions will be noted here.

Current Supply

Same as 9150.

Instruments Needed

Same as 9150.

Removing Movement From The Case (according to the type)

When removing the movement from the case, it is not necessary to detach the setting lever in order to extract the hand-setting stem. Take out the outer setting-lever screw. Because this is pushed by the interrupter spring, the setting lever will shift, thus releasing the hand-setting stem.

Dismantling

Remove in this order: a-the battery bridge; b-the battery; c-the feed bridle; d-the stop lever; e-the setting lever.

IMPORTANT: Do not handle the battery with the tweezers. Special care should be exercised when dismantling the circuit. Refer to previous instructions for ESA 9150.

Cleaning and Demagnetizing

Same as 9150.

Assembling

SPECIAL NOTE: The date jumper spring is made of a special alloy and does not need checking as in ESA 9150. The assembly of the date-indicator mechanism and of the minute wheel mechanism remains the same as in ESA 9150. Otherwise the assembling features remain the same.

Fitting the Circuit

Same as ESA 9150.

Hand-Setting Mechanism

Fit into position: a-the hand-setting pinion; b-the hand-setting setting (grease it lightly); c-the setting lever, taking care to grease the spot which works with the stop-lever stud.

IMPORTANT: Unlike that of calibre ESA 9150, the interrupter spring is directly connected to the + side. **When the hand-setting stem is pulled out, the interrupter spring should on no account touch the interrupter bridle.** Checking the action of the balance stop spring, however, is the same as ESA 9150.

Date Indicator Mechanism

This calibre is simpler than the ESA 9150; it should require no further explanations than those given in the previous chapter.

SPECIAL NOTE: When rapid date-setting is being effected, make certain that the hand-setting stem is turned back far enough to prevent the driving spring from catching on a tooth of the date indicator.

Lubricating the Movement

Same as ESA 9150.

Checking the Damping Action of the Balance

Unchanged from ESA 9150.

Checking the Battery

Same as ESA 9150.

Checking the Interrupter System

The interrupter spring must on no account touch the interrupter bridle when the stem is in the "set" position. When the stem is pushed in, the interrupter spring will press against the interrupter bridle and will shift it slightly, thus insuring good contact.

Checking the Balance Amplitude

Owing to the higher frequency and the peculiar shape of the balance used in this calibre, it is difficult to check its amplitude. Nevertheless, the amplitude should be between the higher limit of 270° in the Dial-Up position and the lower limit of 200° in the Pendant down position.

Casing the Movement

Depending on the type of case, be careful of the mechanical stresses due to the casing-up process.

Adjusting of the Daily Rate

This is the same as ESA 9150. As the mechanical beat has a negligible influence in this calibre, a distance up to 5mm between the strokes forming the timing machine traces can be tolerated.

Checking the Coils

1. Take out the three coil-support screws, Figure 3.
2. The coils are defective if, when they are measured on the ohmmeter and according to Figure 3,

$$\text{Between No. 1 and 2 } R = \infty$$
$$\text{No. 1 and 2 } R = 0$$
$$\text{Between 2 and 3 } R = \infty$$
$$\text{2 and 3 } R = 0$$

In all these cases, the support with the coils fitted must be replaced.

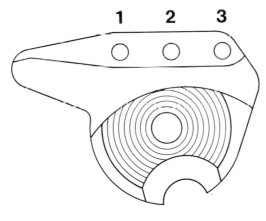

FIGURE 3

ESA 9162

The Swiss tuning fork watch is a creation of Ebauches, S.A., and its official designation is ESA 9162.

Using a tuning fork as its frequency standard, like Bulova's Accutron (from which it is licensed), it claims guaranteed second-a-day accuracy. Its tuning fork differs from Accutron in that it is balanced, claiming a minimization of the position error. Those familiar with servicing the Accutron should find this watch easy to service.

- Resonator (tuning fork) frequency is 300 HZ.
- Battery diameter is 11.60 x 3.60mm . . . 1.35 volts.
- Service capacity to 1.05 V; 110 milliamperehours (rated capacity at 100 microamperes).
- Acceptable batteries: Eveready No. 342 (Union Carbide); Mallory WH 12 NM; Leclanche MR NM.
- This watch has three stem positions:
- The wearing one, with the crown pushed flush towards the case;
- The halfway, second position for setting the calendar mechanism in either direction rapidly (without interrupting the remainder of the movement functions). During the hours of 11:45 p.m. and 2:00 a.m. the calendar mechanism should not be manipulated;
- The third and last position is with the crown pulled out as far as it will go. This position breaks the electrical circuit and lets you set the hands to the exact time. This outermost position also is used to disconnect the battery current in order to store the watch. Regulation can be done with the movement in the case but the case back must be removed.

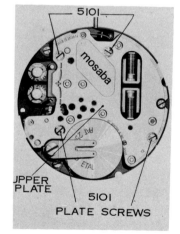

FIGURE 1

Since, for the time being, three companies will be using this calibre, it would be best to study the cases of each make to determine the safest and best method for opening each watch case.

Figure 1 shows the movement side of this calibre. In the place occupied by the name "mosaba" (movements sans balance), the name of the distributor will appear, such as Omega, Longines, Eterna, International, etc.

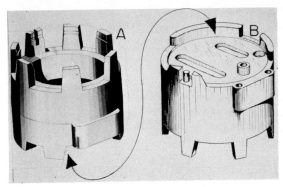

FIGURE 2

To service and check this movement, you will need certain tools. These are: a special holder (Figure 2A), a plastic ring to hold the module when adjusting the click system (Figure 3), a current supply connector (Figure 4) for the movement holder that fits into the holder in Figure 2B.

There is a key for regulating the frequency of the tuning fork (Figure 5). This key fits over the triangular, affixes on the fork's ends and shifts these pieces clockwise or counterclockwise.

To align the pawls in correct conjunction with the click wheel (indexing wheel), you can use another tool with a hollow tip. It is shown in Figure 6, shifting the indexing jewel. The tip fits equally well over the locking pawl post and also should be used to shift the locking pawl into correct conjunction with the click wheel.

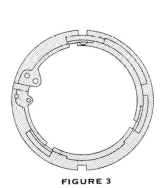

FIGURE 3

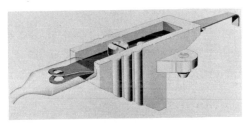

FIGURE 4

(DO NOT use a screwdriver in the slot of the locking jewel post; it is fixed solidly to the plate.)

You will also need an outside power source, and a reliable volt, ohm and ammeter. For production repairs, the Esametre 2 meets all of these requirements.

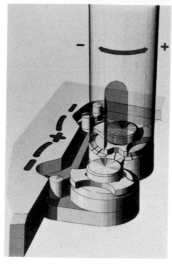

FIGURE 5

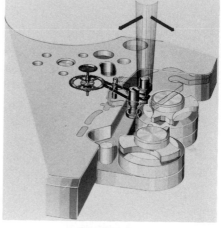

FIGURE 6

Figure 7 shows the other end of the hollow-tip tool shown in Figure 6. At this end, there is a right-angled screwdriver, which can be fitted into the screw of the corrector support and can be lever-turned to advance or retract the locking pawl.

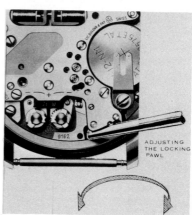

ADJUSTING THE LOCKING PAWL

FIGURE 7

Servicing

1. Never put the movement in a demagnetizer.
2. Never pick up the click wheel with tweezers; its pinion, however, may be carefully held with tweezers.
3. When cleaning the click wheel, you must mount it on the upper plate (Figure 1).
4. Do not handle the battery with metallic tweezers.
5. Carefully check the resonator magnets to be sure they are absolutely clean.
6. Do not use liquids or solutions to clean the transistor, resistance and condenser units, or the date indicator.

BATTERY CLAMP

FIGURE 8   FIGURE 8

7. Before taking the movement out of its case, remove the complete module.

8. Never fit the completely assembled movement to the case. This MUST be done with the module removed.

9. DO NOT for any reason, force or move the train in either direction with a tweezer or other tool.

Changing Batteries

Loosen the battery clamp screw (Figure 8A) enough to disengage the battery clamp, by shifting it towards the inside of the plate as shown in Figure 8B. Remove the battery and check its voltage. (If you are dismantling, remove the clamp.)

You must insert the new battery with the positive (+) part facing upward. DO NOT handle the battery with metal tweezers. Return the battery clamp to position and secure it tightly.

Adjusting Daily Rate

You may adjust the daily rate when it is less than 8 seconds plus or minus (+ or -). If the watch exceeds these limits, it is an indication that cleaning or repairs are needed. (These operations will be covered later in the chapter.

If the daily rate is within 8 seconds, you may adjust it using the key shown in Figure 5. Each division below the triangular pieces corresponds to one second a day. Shifting the indexes outward (clockwise on the right tine, and counterclockwise on the left tine) slows down the rate. Shifting the indexes inward speeds up the rate. It makes no difference whether you use one or both correctors for regulation. However, to prevent an imbalance, it is advisable to avoid using one corrector more than the other.

Movement Removal

Before taking the movement out of the case, you must:

1. Remove the case back.
2. Remove the battery clamp (Figure 8A).
3. Remove the four upper plate screws (5101), and remove the upper plate (101) as shown in Figure 1.
4. Turn the watch dial side up so that the upper plate (module) will drop out. DO NOT touch the hands until this has been done.
5. Remove the hand setting stem (405) by pressing on the setting lever axle, as shown in Figure 9.
6. Loosen the three case-clamp screws (5166). Slide the clamps inward and then tighten these screws again.

You can now remove the movement from the case. Place it on the special movement holder (Figure 2A). Replace the stem and crown in the movement. Push it all the way so the setting lever stud enters the stem slot. Make certain, when seating the movement in the movement holder, to press it and seat it firmly with the stem between the two posts of the movement holder.

Movement Replacement

As shown in Figure 9, remove the stem and crown. Replace the movement in the case (without the module-upper plate). Replace the stem and crown, and be sure to grease the crown joint. Loosen the clamp screws; slide the clamps outward and secure their screws tightly. Each of these clamps has two "dimples" to facilitate its manipulations with tweezers. Place the upper plate (module) in position, and fix it in position by means of its four screws.

Insert the battery and tighten its clamp. Place the waterproofing gasket in position, and close the case. Check the rate of the watch on the timing machine.

Click Mechanism

You do not have to dismantle the movement to check the (indexing) click mechanism. You need only supply the movement

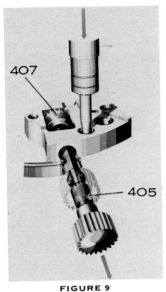

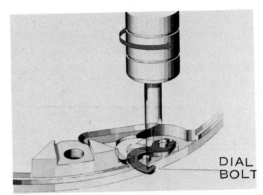

FIGURE 9

FIGURE 10

with a voltage between 1 and 1.35 volts. Methods of checking the click mechanism and some other checks of the electronic circuit will be discussed later.

Dismantling Procedures

Non-magnetic tweezers are strongly recommended for use with such watches or their components.

After removing the back, the battery clamp's screw and the battery clamp, remove the four upper plate screws (5101) and the upper plate (101), as shown in Figure 1. Turn the watch dial side up to allow the loose upper plate-module to drop out of its own accord.

Press on the set lever axle, withdraw the stem and crown, and remove the clutch wheel (407, Figure 9).

Loosen the case-clamps screws, and slide the three clamps inward. Secure the screws again. Now, remove the movement. Position it firmly into the top portion of the movement holder (Figure 2A). Now, you may remove the hands.

To remove the dial, release the two dial bolts with a screwdriver, as shown in Figure 10. Remove the dial and the hour wheel (255).

Now turn to Figure 11. Remove the date indicator by removing its three screws. Remove the date indicator guard (2535), then the date jumper (2576), the date indicator, the date indicator driving wheel (2556), and the intermediate date wheel (2543). Remove the minute wheel and then the center wheel combination cannon pinion (200).

After removing its two screws (5445), remove the setting lever spring (445), and then the yoke (435), the yoke spring and the setting lever. Next, turn the movement over and secure it in the movement holder.

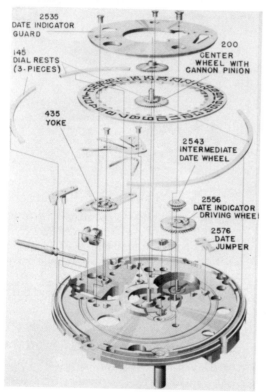

2535
DATE INDICATOR
GUARD

145
DIAL RESTS
(3-PIECES)

200
CENTER
WHEEL WITH
CANNON PINION

435
YOKE

2543
INTERMEDIATE
DATE WHEEL

2556
DATE INDICATOR
DRIVING WHEEL

2576
DATE
JUMPER

FIGURE 11

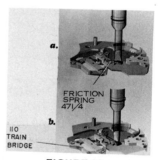

a.

FRICTION
SPRING
471/4

b.

110
TRAIN
BRIDGE

FIGURE 12

Figure 12A shows a friction spring (471/4), which is tensioned against the fourth wheel arbor. Release this spring by placing a screwdriver in the slot of the spring's collet and twisting it 45 degrees (1/8 turn) clockwise, as shown in Figure 12B.

Now remove the three train bridge screws, securing the train bridge (110), Figure 12B; and disengage the third and fourth wheels. **Never immerse the third wheel in any solution.** It may be dry-cleaned. The colored plastic, feed-bridle insulator (4045) may be left in place, since most cleaning solutions and mild heat will not affect this.

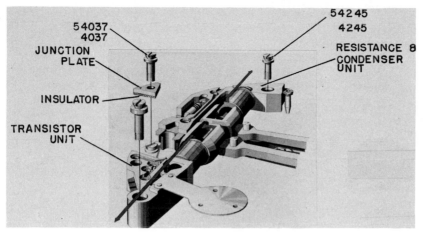

FIGURE 13

Place the module onto the movement holder (Figure 2B), so that its positioning notch (Figure 15) is fitted against the cylindrical post at the edge of the movement holder, shown in Figure 2B. Position the module securely into the holder by pressing on the steady pins of the module.

After removing the screws (54037, 54245), remove the junction plate and its insulator underneath, as shown in Figure 13.

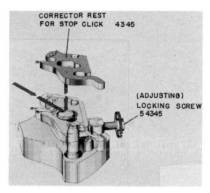

CORRECTOR REST
FOR STOP CLICK   4345

(ADJUSTING)
LOCKING SCREW
54345

FIGURE 14

Making certain not to damage the coils, remove the Resistance and Condenser Unit (4245) first, sliding it out in the direction of the arrow. Next remove the Transistor Unit (4240), sliding that out, too.

Remove the corrector rest for the stop click (4345), as in Figure 14. To do so, loosen the lock screw (54345) just enough to allow the corrector rest to slide out in the direction of the arrow. Then lift the corrector rest upward and out.

Refer to Figure 15 (exploded view). Remove the two screws (5118) and remove the combined bridge (118).

Next remove the two resonator screws (54600), and then carefully lift out the resonator (4600). This is best done by using a screwdriver as a wedge in the notch especially provided for this purpose.

Cleaning

IMPORTANT: The following parts **must not** be cleaned in the cleaning machine:

a) the date indicator;

b) the two electronic units (Transistor and Resistance and Condenser Units 4240, 4245);

c) the battery.

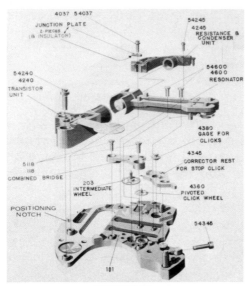

FIGURE 15

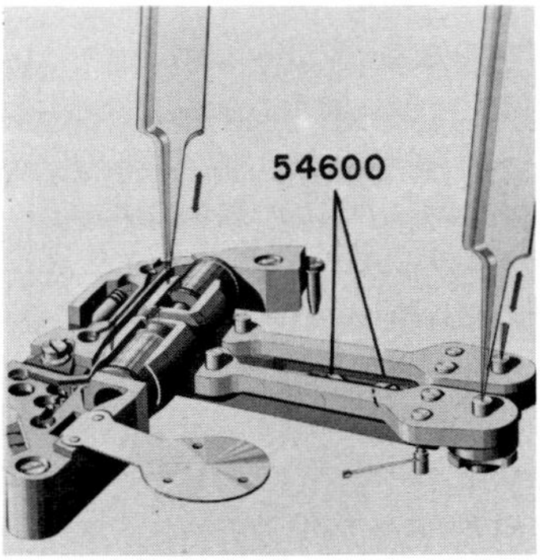

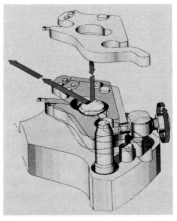

FIGURE 16

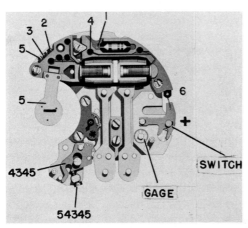

FIGURE 17

FIGURE 18

210

These parts may be dry brushed or gently wiped with a Selvyt cloth or air blower.

The cleaning solutions must be fresh, uncontaminated with metallic particles which would inevitably become attached to the resonator magnets.

Cleaning should be done with the (indexing) click wheel and mechanism assembled. Exercise extreme caution to avoid damaging its delicate teeth. The resonator magnets also should be cleaned with the same delicate care. After cleaning, inspect them to be sure they are perfectly clean. Remove any particles clinging to the magnets using adhesive tape or Rodico. Be very careful not to damage the driving pawl. It is a good idea to first clear the cleansing solutions in the ultrasonic machine's liquid jars of metallic particles by placing a permanent magnet temporarily in the solution before cleaning.

Assembling and Oiling

There are two stages in assembling. One is to assemble the complete upper plate (module). Fit the upper plate into position on the movement holder (Figure 2B). Fit the click-wheel and combined bridge into position in order to check the endshake of this wheel. Handle it only by its pinion; position it with the oiler-needle and check its endshake the same way. When this is done, remove the bridge and wheel.

Place the resonator on the plate and fix it with its two screws. Secure these tightly — the outer screw first. First secure the Transistor Unit by means of its screws; be careful that the coil enters the yoke of the resonator. Put the Resistance and Condenser Unit in place by sliding it into the yoke of the resonator. Then replace the screw securely.

Now fit the junction plate insulator and the triangular junction plate in place by means of its screw (54037). (See Figure 13.) Check the resonator to make sure it is free, as shown in Figure 16. To do so, place the non-magnetic tweezer lightly on the cups of the resonator and "feel" whether they are free. Or place the point of a tweezer on the pin of the lower end of the fork-resonator as shown. Also, with the point of tweezer at the side of the pin at the lower end of the resonator, flip the point of the tweezer aside. This will set the resonator into sonic action and will enable you to observe its freedom. On no account must its tines come into contact with any part of this movement. Also be sure that the contact point (6) in Figure 17 is not fouled with the contact table of the switch.

Next refer to Figure 14 and 18. Carefully slide the pawl adjusting support (corrector rest for stop click, 4335) into position as shown in Figure 18. Tighten the screw to eliminate endshake of this part; then give this screw one more turn to tighten it.

Notice that in Figure 17, there is a reference to a "gage". This is a stud-shaped piece that is supplied with every movement and rests in a reserve well or counterbore. This gage has no functional purpose in this watch except as a stand-in for the click wheel for

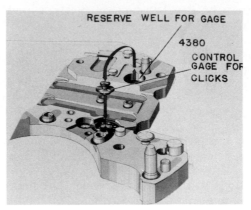

RESERVE WELL FOR GAGE

4380

CONTROL GAGE FOR CLICKS

FIGURE 19

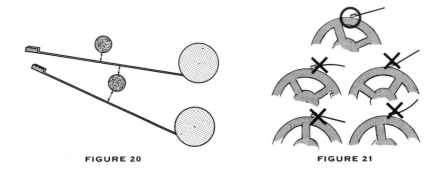

FIGURE 20   FIGURE 21

the adjusting phase, after which it is returned to its well. The gage is kept in its reserve well by light friction, and it can be easily removed and replaced for the testing and alignment phasing.

Lift out the control gage for clicks (4380), Figure 19, and place it into the space normally occupied by the click wheel. (Remember that earlier the click wheel was removed after its end-shake was satisfactory.)

Adjusting the Click Mechanism

The blades of the two pawls should be as straight as possible and should on no account touch the pins. (See Figure 20.)

Figure 21 shows some common index blade faults which may be corrected with the tweezers. Check the tension of the pawls and their setting in relation to each other with the gage. The pawl jewels should be perfectly aligned with the plane of the gage as shown in the top view, Figure 22. They must be perpendicular to the plane of the gage. If not, they may be altered to correct alignment with a pair of tweezers, working on the pawl blades as close to the studs as possible. The height of the outer crown of the gage has been calculated so that the jewel should be entirely included in that distance. If correction is necessary, work on the

212

pawl's studs with the special tool shown in Figure 6. (Do not use a screwdriver in the slot of the locking pawl support. This cannot be twisted.)

The outside diameter of the gage has been calculated for determining the optimum pawl tension. The pawls, however, must on no account press against the gage; a space of about 1/100mm should remain between the tips of the blades and the rim of the gage as shown in the top view, Figure 22. For all corrections use tweezers on the blades at their junction with the studs and the tool, shown in Figure 6. Using any good oil, lubricate the two click-wheel bearings on the upper plate side.

NOTE: Take special care, when placing the click wheel in position, not to upset the preceding adjustment or damage the very fine click wheel teeth.

Place the click wheel (4360) in position (Figure 15). Take care not to upset the adjustment of the click mechanism. Now place the intermediate wheel (203) in position (Figure 15).

Next, place the combined bridge (118) in position (Figure 15). Make certain the click wheel pivots are in place, but **do not touch this wheel with the positioning tweezers**. Secure the bridge by means of its two screws.

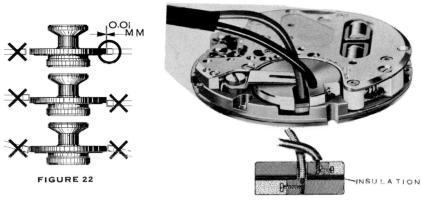

FIGURE 22

FIGURE 23

The click mechanism can be adjusted either with the movement assembled or with the module alone (upper plate). For this adjustment, you will need an outside battery current supply system. This can be obtained in a number of forms. One is shown in Figure 4.

The clip is attached to the movement holder and makes contact with the movement plate, supplying circuits from the source. The other cable ends of this clip may be attached to a correct current source. Figure 23 shows two lead wires attached to a dummy battery. It is fitted to the movement if testing is required when the movement is fully assembled and in its case. The other ends of these cables are attached to the power source outside the watch — a battery of the correct voltage or a variable power source such as the Esametre, which contains such a section. The dummy battery consists of two layers of disked brass separated by glued insulation and its terminals, held by set screws.

For measuring the resistance of the Transistor-Resistance-Condenser Units or insulations, etc., as well as power consumption, any reliable 20,000-ohm-per-volt multimeter will do.

With the module set into the movement rest (Figure 2B), check the clicking mechanism. Use the minimum voltage of 1 volt. Shift the adjusting screw of the corrector rest for stop click (4345) in either direction, until the train runs continuously. Watching the click wheel and the intermediate wheel under magnification should quickly show whether these are running satisfactorily. Next, check the train action at higher voltages up to 1.7, and especially at the normal running supply voltage of 1.35 volts.

Since a variable power source will be needed to test this watch, a simple form might be described.

Two 1.5 cells can be fitted in series to obtain a 3.0 volt supply. These cells are then placed in a clip from which current can be drawn. However, since for this watch voltages from 0.9 to 1.7 will be needed, a variable resistance (rheostat) is placed in series with this set-up. Suitable leads are then attached and placed at the terminals of a reliable voltmeter. The resistance is then adjusted slowly until the desired voltage is obtained. The leads may then be connected to the module by the clip shown in Figure 4 (available from the watch importer) or the type shown in Figure 23.

If the train runs continuously at normal speed 1.0, 1.7 and then at 1.35 volts, the click mechanism is in proper adjustment. If the train doesn't run continuously, refer to the troubleshooting section.

Assembling the Movement

Fit the movement on the special movement holder (Figure 2A). If you had removed the red plastic feed-bridle insulator, assemble it by inserting the longest of its tabs in place first.

Oil the dial side of the intermediate wheel jewel. Check the tension of the friction spring (Figures 12A, 12B) of the fourth wheel. Turn its maintaining screw, as far as the stop pin, against the flat side of the screw. The spring should be tangential to the center pipe and parallel to the plane of the plate. If the tension is insufficient, examine the spring and adjust the tension. Then, disengage the spring before assembling the train.

Now fit the fourth wheel in position. After greasing the friction spring of the third wheel with light grease, fit this wheel. If the third wheel needs separate cleaning, clean it with cold isopropylic alcohol for no longer than 20 seconds. When it is dry, add a drop of oil between the wheel plate and the steel disk. Then check its friction washer.

To test for correct friction of the third wheel, place the stem in the hand-setting position. Then "twirl" the crown and observe the wheels from the train side. If both the third and fourth wheels move, the friction is correct. If the fourth wheel doesn't move, friction is insufficient and the third wheel must be replaced.

Replace the train bridge and tighten its three screws. Check the endshake of the wheels. Oil both wheels' hole jewels in this bridge. Now re-engage the friction spring of the fourth wheel. Turn its screw as far as it will go. The banking pin controls the amount you can turn this screw. Make certain the spring is engaged properly in the groove of the friction pulley.

Now turn the plate over on the movement rest. Grease the spindles of the yoke (435) and the setting lever. Replace the hand setting stem, clutch wheel, setting lever, yoke and yoke spring. Replace the setting lever spring with its two screws (Figure 11).

Grease the pivot of the stem and its square, the stud of the setting lever, the groove of the yoke and the axle of the setting wheel.

With any good watch oil, lubricate the center pipe, the pivot shank of the minute wheel, the spindle of the intermediate date wheel and the spindle of the date-indicator driving wheel. (All are shown in Figure 11.)

Next, replace the combination center wheel and cannon pinion, the minute wheel, the intermediate date wheel, the date-indicator driving wheel, the date indicator and date jumper and remainder of calendar mechanism.

Remove the stem and fit the movement. Remember that the module containing the resonator and electronic circuit has not yet been assembled to the main movement. Fit the movement (without the module) into the case. Replace the stem; push it in all the way. Secure the movement to the case by the three casing clamps and tighten these screws securely.

Now, you may fit the complete upper plate (module) by means of its four screws. Before you tighten the screws, be sure the intermediate wheel pivot is in place in its jewel hole. Check the endshake of this wheel. *Do not turn the intermediate wheel for any reason.*

Replace the battery and its clamp and tighten its screw. Check the operation of the click mechanism by observing the click wheel and the action of the intermediate wheel, while the stem is pushed in all the way and a current is supplied by its own battery.

Using a timing machine, adjust the instantaneous rate. Close the case and recheck the instantaneous rate. Often, you will find there is a one-second difference (slower) when the case is closed. Therefore, when adjusting the instantaneous rate with the case open, allow for this difference. Altitude also affects the rate at one second fast for every 1500 feet above sea level.

Electronic Circuit Check

To check the watch's circuit and electrical efficiency, you need a volt, ohm, ammeter with an outside power source (range up to 2 volts). Ebauches S.A. sells an elaborate device (the Esametre-2) that meets all these requirements. It converts ordinary house

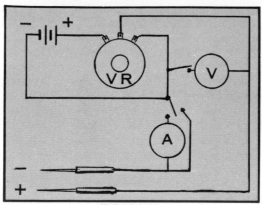

FIGURE 24

current to its needs. However, any reliable volt, ohm and ammeter combination with a 20K Ω per volt range can be used for most of these functions.

The schematic in Figure 24 shows a 3-volt source which is led into a variable resistor (rheostat). By manipulating this resistor in connection with the voltmeter, you can obtain the desired voltage. Simple switches, when turned, will feed this reduced, desired current directly to the leads or through the ammeter.

You can easily adapt a set-up such as this one to your available meter. The variable resistor is inexpensive and easy to hook up.

Radio supply stores also sell power suppliers that convert house current into DC current from 0 to 30 volts (such as the Eico 1020). This unit has its own built-in voltmeter that indicates the drain. With such an instrument, however, it is best to first connect the leads to a reliable voltmeter to arrive at the desired and true voltage.

1. Testing the Battery

You should test the battery while it is out of the watch. If it rates 1.35 volts, it is acceptable. If it tests less than 1.25 volts, replace it.

2. Measuring the Movement's Current Consumption

Remove the battery from the movement. To read the power consumption in microamperes (μA), connect the set-up so the ammeter's negative (-) lead (set to read microamps) is connected to the negative (-) lead of the energy source (1.35 volts). The ammeter's positive (+) lead should be connected to *Point 5*, shown in Figure 17. Then, connect the lead from the positive (+) terminal of the energy source to the movement plate — *Point 6* in Figure 17.

The needle will move suddenly to the far end of the meter, but will quickly settle back to a point on the meter which should not exceed 8.5 μA, regardless of the movement's position. With this set-up, the module resonators should become activated and the ammeter should register.

216

If this does not happen, try flipping the lower pin of the right fork tine. If the unit does not function, check the resonator for freedom. If the power consumption is more than 8.5 μA, also check the resonators and pawls for interference.

3. Resistance Check Between Points 1 and 4 in Figure 17.

This test is only applied when the Resistance and Condenser Unit 4245 is dismantled from the module. Its purpose is to see if there is a short circuit within this unit.

With the multimeter switched to read in the 20KΩ per volt range, contact the meter's black (-) lead to *Point 1*, Figure 17, and the red (+) lead to *Point 4*, Figure 17. If the meter's needle remains stationary at ∞, the insulation is good. If the needle moves even slightly, there is a partial or total short circuit between these points, and this unit must be changed.

4. Break Switch and Insulation Check

With the stem pulled out all the way, the contact between *Point 6*, Figure 17, and the break switch (movement plate) should be open. To test it, touch the red (+) lead of the meter (ohms) to the plate, and touch the black (-) lead to *Point 5*. If all is well, the needle should remain at ∞.

To test the insulation, when the module is separate from the movement, place a thin plastic shim between *Point 6* and the contact plate. If the meter prods are placed at the plate and at *Point 6*, the needle should remain motionless.

5. Checking the Break Switch

Place one lead of the ohmmeter at *Point 6*, Figure 17, and the other lead on the movement plate with the stem pushed in all the way. The needle should jump to the end of the scale if the contacts are good. If not, clean or adjust the contact blades of the breakswitch.

6. Checking the Complete Circuit (module alone)

With the meter reading 20KΩ or more per volt, place one prod of the meter at *Point 4*, Figure 17, and the other at *Point 6*. The result should be a reading of approximately 7KΩ. If it is below 5KΩ, or more than 10KΩ, the Resistance and Condenser Unit 4245 should be changed.

7. Checking the Resonator Circuit

Remove the battery. With the meter set to read microamperes, place the red (+) prod at *Point 6* and the black (-) prod at *Point 5*, Figure 17. Then, hold the tweezer or your fingernail at the pin on the lower end of the right resonator tine. Flip this to set the resonator vibrating. The meter's needle should move up to a reading of approximately 0.5 on the 0 to 20 μA scale. Excessive movement, or none at all, indicates a need to change the transistor unit 4240.

The main criterion of normal behavior is the oscillation of the resonator.

8. Testing the Efficiency of the Circuitry

Remove the battery. Using the outside power source, regulate the voltage to 1.35 volts. The movement battery current supply system shown in Figure 4 can be used here.

With the module in the movement holder shown in Figure 2B, attach the clip so its points make proper electrical contact. The other ends of the clip have lead wires to be attached to the variable voltage source.

Another method is to place the power source (+) prods at *Point 6*, Figure 17 (the plate), and the (-) prod at *Point 5*. The movement should start to resonate and the click wheel and intermediate wheel should begin to turn.

Observe this under magnification of a pivot loupe. Then you can lower the voltage. The movement should continue to run, even when the voltage reduced to 1.0 volt. Continue to watch the click wheel and intermediate wheel, and raise the voltage slowly until it reads 1.7 volts. The speed of the click and intermediate wheels should remain the same

Trouble Shooting

Numbers in parentheses refer to headings under the previous section, "Checking the electrical circuit." Follow the instructions in these paragraphs.

A-Complete Stoppage

1. Test battery (1). If the battery is below 1.25 volts, replace it.

2. When the battery is good, test the power consumption (2).

3. If the power consumption is abnormal, remove the module and conduct checks, following instruction (3). If the tests under (3) show abnormal behavior (∞), the resonator may not be free. Clean it and remove obstructions. Examine the resonator thoroughly.

4. If tests under (3) show normal function and the resonator is free, conduct the tests under (6).

5. If check under (3) suggests a short circuit, replace the unit.

B-Resonator Works/Hands Stop

1. Check the fitting of the hands. If hands appear to be at fault, open the case and remove the module. Take the movement from the case and adjust the hands. Replace movement and then the module.

2. When the hands are in order, check the battery (1). If it is acceptable, check (2).

3. If the reading is less than 4 μA in check (2), remove the module, check contacts, switch and junction plate and its insulator 4037 in Figure 17. Replace the faulty parts.

If checks (1) and (2) are good, examine the click pawl jewels under magnification. There may be a jewel missing from one of the click pawls. Replace the faulty parts.

4. If the test under (2) shows a reading of more than 9 μA, examine the clickwork. If it is dirty, remove both circuits and clean the module completely; dismantle the combined bridge 118, in Figure 15. Check and correct the tension of the clickwork with gage 4380. Oil and reassemble the parts to make final adjustments to the clickwork.

5. When the click jewels are good, check the tension of the clicks as shown in Figures 20 and 21. Adjust the tension.

Or the clicks may be out of engagement with the click wheel — they may have slipped above or below it.

6. Adjust the clickwork. This can be done when the module is separate from or assembled to the rest of the movement. To do this, apply an outside variable voltage. First, use the minimum 1.0 volt. Shift the adjusting screw (Figure 7) in either direction until the train runs continuously at normal speed. Then, raise the voltage to 1.7 volts. Finally, lower it to the normal 1.35 volts.

C-Only Second Hand Turns

1. Open the case, remove battery and module. Extract the movement from the case. Remove the dial and hands. Check the calendar mechanism. If it is faulty, correct or replace the parts at fault.

2. When the calendar is in order, clean the regulator part of the movement and reassemble it.

3. If the movement itself is clean, replace the third wheel. Its friction is insufficient to carry the dial train. **Do not try to adjust this friction — replace the wheel.**

D-Error of Rate

This watch can be timed directly on most modern timing machines, such as the Vibrograf 200, the Tickoprint TP46 or the Greiner.

1. If the instantaneous rate is good, but you find an error under actual wearing conditions: open the case, check the clickwork according to checks in B (4, 5, 6) above.

2. If the clickwork is satisfactory, remove the module. Clean and reassemble it, and adjust the rate.

3. If the instantaneous rate is more than 10 seconds slow a day: open the case, remove the battery, module and both units. Check the module and both units. Clean and oil them. Reassemble and check the rate.

4. If the rate is still poor after check in B-3, replace the resonator. After replacement, if the rate is still unchanged, replace the click wheel.

E-Faulty Calendar Works

1. Open the case, remove the module and then the movement.

2. If the hour wheel and the hour hand endshake are in order, check the calendar mechanism and replace the faulty parts.

F-Intermittent Stoppage

1. Open the case, remove the module and replace both units.

JUNGHANS-ATO-CHRON
(600 Series)

FIGURE 1   FIGURE 2

Like the other electronic balance-driven watches, these are miniaturized versions of the Ato Max and similar models used in transistorized balance-driven clocks. Figure 1 is known as the ATO-CHRON.

The details of the movement are:

Movement diameter: 30.8mm (13½ lignes).

Movement thickness: 5.4mm

Number of jewels: 17

Vibrations per hour of balance:

    21,600 (3 impulses a second).

Hairspring: Nivarox 1, 11 coils.

Battery: Mallory, WH 3; 1.35V; 150 mAH

Energy consumption at $1.35V - V < 12 \mu A$

Amplitude in horizontal position at 1.35V-230°

Figure 2 shows the dial and bridge sides of this movement with and without the battery. The three-pronged extension is the negative battery contact.

Figure 3 shows the electrodynamic diagram principle used to drive the balance. This electronic system makes the balance self-starting, independent of the position of the watch, even should it be absolutely motionless. The starting process begins as soon as the battery is installed.

When the battery is inserted, current flows through coils L_2- and L_1 and the resistor R_V and charges the polarization capacitor

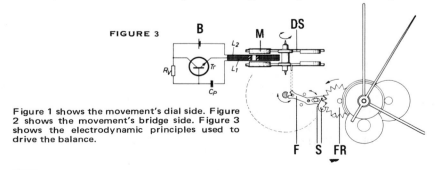

FIGURE 3

Figure 1 shows the movement's dial side. Figure 2 shows the movement's bridge side. Figure 3 shows the electrodynamic principles used to drive the balance.

C_P. The pulse of current through $L_2 L_1$ moves the upper and lower magnets M on the balance unit DS, starting the watch. C_P then discharges through the emitter-base current of the transistor Tr, making the transistor circuit oscillate. This builds up to the approximate rhythm of the balance wheel's frequency, sensed at coil L_2, whose magnetic fields in conjunction with the balance wheel's magnets M cause torsional impulses at the balance.

Very soon, this starting phase changes to a stationary oscillating condition. This is characterized by the so-called self-control effect. Here the inductive control impulses, produced by the upper and lower magnets on the balance, in control of coil L_1 set off the operating impulses in the transistor's collector circuit.

The dial's hands are driven from the motor-balance through the escapement lever fork F. Two D-shaped jewels, S, move the index wheel FR. This converts the oscillating motion of the balance into rotary motion of the index wheel and on through the train wheels to move the hands. Since the gear ratios are in reverse proportion and power direction from mainspring-driven watches, wear is negligible. Figures 4 and 5 show an indexing sequence. In Figure 4 the index wheel is held motionless by the attraction of the pin magnet under the tooth shown at the top of this illustration. The pallet-lever at this moment is in a neutral position.

In Figure 4, the "entrance jewel" will contact the tip of the nearest tooth, moving it slightly counterclockwise. The under-index wheel-magnet will move this back to its original position. In Figure 5, when the balance moves the pallet fork, the entrance jewel will contact the front of the same tooth and move it for a complete indexing in the clockwise direction where it will be held by the index wheel magnet. The "exit" jewel serves no other purpose than as a banking guard for the escape wheel when the index wheel is repositioned by the magnet after the entrance jewel has flipped the index wheel slightly backward. In other words, the "entrance" jewel only does the indexing, therefore, the index wheel is moved only in alternate vibrations or three times a second.

Do not confuse the direction of this index wheel which appears opposite from that in Figure 3 as this drawing shows the action as it appears from the dial side.

The electronic components and the integrally wound operating and control coils are assembled to form one electrical unit. This is shown with and without the plastic cover in Figure 6 and is termed the "electronic block". This is a plastic plate, further protected by a plastic cover, and becomes the electronic module. Those who wish to check the module can do so with an ohmmeter with a 20,000 ohm range. With the plastic module removed, turn this over on its back (Figure 6A) so that the coil and connections are uppermost. The battery connector prong should be closest to you, pointing left. With one prod of the ohmmeter on A and the other on B, the reading should be between 2500 and 3000 ohms. When the prods are positioned at B and C or A and D, the meter readings should be between 1200 and 1600 ohms. The unit can just as easily be tested functionally to see if the balance is impelled properly or not.

In order to shield the movement from outside magnetic fields, it is encased in a shielding plate (Figure 7). This is a precaution against the ever-increasing use of permanent and electromagnets in everyday life.

As shown in Figure 8, the crown is displaced from its traditional position as a reminder that its purpose is merely for hand-setting and no longer for winding. Setting the hands also serves as a hack mechanism, stopping the watch. This allows the time to be set to the second.

The power source is a Mallory mercury-oxide cell, type WH-3, with a nominal capacity of 150 mAh. This type is noted for its

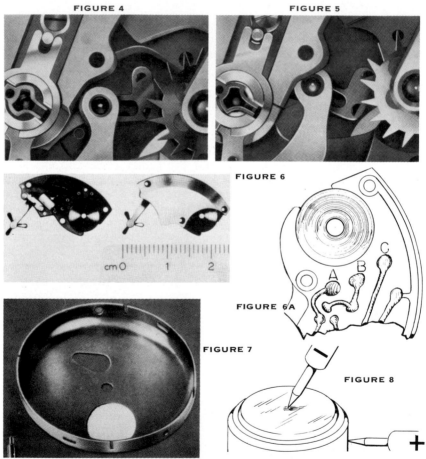

Figures 4 and 5 (top, left and right) show an indexing sequence. The electronic components and the operating and control coils are assembled to form one electrical unit, shown with and without plastic cover in Figure 6 (middle, left). The electronic module is shown on its back with the cover removed in Figure 6A (middle, right). A shielding plate, shown in Figure 7 (bottom, left), protects the movement from outside magnetic fields. Figure 8 (bottom, right) indicates how prongs should be placed when checking the battery's voltage with a meter.

long storage life, non-leaky design and voltage independence from the extent of discharge. It should serve the watch from 12 to 16 months. If the watch loses time after running satisfactorily for a year or so, it is a sure sign that the battery is exhausted and should be replaced.

Servicing the Ato-Chron

Basic requirements for servicing the Ato-Chron are:
Non-magnetic tweezers and screwdrivers.
Spare battery (Mallory WH-3)
Spare Ato-Chron electronic block for comparison purposes.
Multi-meter with an internal resistance of more than 20,000 Ohm/V.

Examining and Repair Procedures

1—Check the battery voltage.
2—Check the mechanical section of the watch.
3—Replace the electronic block (for comparison purposes).

Battery Voltage:

Excessive deviation in accuracy of time indicates that the battery is exhausted and should be replaced.

Open the case. Turning the watch over causes the battery to fall out. In some models, the battery can be removed without opening the case. In such instances, the battery lid on the case back is removed and the battery replacement is easily made. Check the battery's voltage with the meter. Place the prongs as in Figure 8. This should be done quickly — never for more than 3 to 5 seconds. Use a voltmeter with a load resistor of 1000 ohms coupled parallel (Figure 9). Should the voltage exceed 1.3V, the battery is still operative. A new battery will check out at 1.35V.

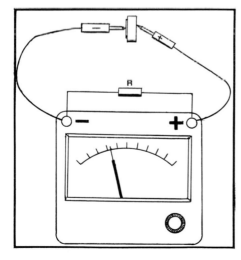

Use a voltmeter with a load resistor of 1000 ohms to check battery voltage as in Figure 9.

To open the case, use a watchmaker's knife, or obtain a special key from Sheffield's Service Department. If a new battery is used, it should be inserted so that the (+) marking on the battery is visible as in Figure 2B. The balance should start oscillating as soon as the battery is in contact with the movement.

The amplitude of the balance should reach 230° in less than 30 seconds after starting when the watch is in the horizontal position.

When you are satisfied that the movement runs perfectly, the case back or cover can be fitted. Before doing so, make certain that the sealing washer fits tightly. The case can be closed with strong pressure by the thumb.

Checking the Mechanical Section

If the movement does not perform satisfactorily despite the insertion of a fresh, tested battery, the following is recommended:

Remove the case back.

Remove back magnetic shield.

Remove the movement holding screws and blanks.

Loosen and remove winding stem.

Remove movement.

Remove dial and hands. Dial screws can be reached through holes in the under-dial magnetic shield.

Loosen front magnetic shield.

Balance Unit

The shock resisting device is the "Star-Shoc" system. The spring is a captive one — that is, it is hinged and cannot fly off when loosened. A defective shock spring, however, can easily be replaced by pressing out the shock-block setting. The spring can then be unhinged and the new one easily connected.

The proper functioning of the balance is tested by its damping time. With the movement in the horizontal position, turn the balance wheel 180° out of its neutral position. Measure the time between the moment you release the balance and the time when it comes to a stop. If this takes longer than 15 seconds, the balance bearing units are in satisfactory condition.

Vertical clearance of the balance should be minimal (between 0.03 and 0.05mm). The coil of the electronic block should be exactly between the upper and lower balance-magnets. Also, the balance magnets must be positioned symmetrically above the coil when in the neutral position.

Wheel Train, Escapement and Transmission

The transmission lever (pallet) and index wheel are magnetically banked. These settings are factory-fixed and are not to be disturbed. When the escape wheel is in the magnetically locked position and the balance continues through the supplementary arc, one tooth of the escape wheel should be exactly above the stop magnet (Figures 4-5). As soon as the lever has affected the small return motion of the index wheel, it must jump back into the position shown in Figures 4-5. The lever too is banked magnetically. To make any repair or adjustment to the mechanical section, it will be necessary to remove the balance. To remove the balance, the electronic block must be removed. This is done by removing the three brass bridge screws and easing the block out sideways so that its coil does not scrape the balance's magnets.

The lever and train are then dismantled. Only two screws need be loosened to remove the train bridge. In some newer models, a raised screw on the train bridge should be turned ¼ turn counter-clockwise. This will release a friction spring, rubbing in a groove in a nylon disc on the sweep second wheel. When assembling the train, make certain this spring is swung into the nylon disc's groove. This can be accomplished by turning the top screw ¼ turn in the clockwise direction.

If the movement does not operate with a fresh battery and perfect mechanical parts, then the electronic block should be exchanged. The following order is recommended.

Fit the stem to the uncased movement.

Turn the balance 90° out of its neutral position as in Figure 10.

Pull the crown into the setting position; this locks the balance in this position.

Loosen the three brass screws on the plastic electronic block and remove the block carefully so as not to have its coil scrape the balance's upper and lower magnets.

Fit a new electronic block, slipping in the coil sideways as a precaution against scraping the balance magnets.

Check the clearance of the new coil of the electronic block. As shown in Figure 11, the coil must be positioned exactly between the balance magnets; the gap between the magnets and the coil is the same on either side. The vertical clearance of the coil can be altered by exchanging the support bushings of the electronic block for different ones (Figure 12). These bushings are available in 5 heights, graduated in 0.03mm with the thicknesses from 0.58 to 0.70mm. As soon as the electronic block has been fitted, the battery can be inserted polewise and in such a way that the battery's shell is in contact with the movement.

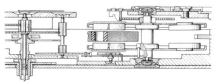

When exchanging the electronic unit, turn the balance 90° out of its neutral position as in Figure 10 (left). The electronic block's new coil must be positioned between the balance magnets as in Figure 11 (right). Support bushings of the electronic block can be exchanged to alter the coil's vertical clearance as in Figure 12 (opposite).

If the movement operates perfectly, it can be put back into the case. The following should then be observed:

The negative contact spring (Figure 13) must not touch any metallic movement parts. The insulator in the front shield should not be moved. The sealing washer must fit the case tightly in any position before the back can be pressed on.

Cleaning, Oiling, Demagnetizing

The movement can be cleaned by the ultrasonic method or by normal cleaning procedures and with the usual solutions with only the following exception:

The electronic block must not come into contact with detergents of any kind. The electronic block must be removed before attempting to clean the movement.

Because of the various magnets used in this watch, demagnetization of the balance unit and of the movement should be avoided.

Oils and Oiling Points

Balance pivots and jewels
>   Elgin M 56b

All pivot bearing of all wheels and the transmission lever.
Friction of the dial train.
Hands setting wheel bearing
>   Synt-A-Lube

Clutch lever
Hand setting pinion
Click and clickspring
>   Lusin-Grease

Do not oil the regulator or the pallets.

Timing and Regulation

Set the timing machine to properly record 21,600 VPH. The transmission noises from the escape wheel (index wheel) and from the roller jewel will be sufficient to record the beats on the graph paper.

When interpreting the timing machine record, the diagram will show two parallel lines. The distance between them is of no significance to the timing of the watch.

Figure 10 shows the balance bridge and regulator. The eccentric screw in the regulator tail's fork allows very fine regulation. Turning this screw clockwise causes the watch to go faster. Turning this screw counterclockwise slows it down.

In Figure 13 the negative contact spring must not touch any metallic movement parts.

SEIKO EL 370

FIGURE 1

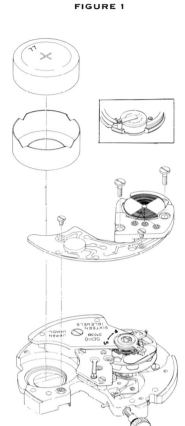

FIGURE 2

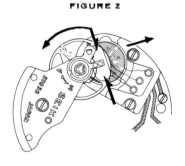

Specifications: Vibrations per hour-21,600; EPX 77 Power Cell; Day-Date with push-type date corrector and reciprocating day corrector as well as a second-setting device, combination switch.

This watch's electronic principle is similar to others with the exception of the indexing system. Like other transistorized watches whose balance move the pallet to index the escape wheel and train, this model depends as well on a retaining pawl which operates on a click wheel mounted on the escape wheel. This retaining pawl demands as much care as the electronic module, and its correct adjustment is paramount else the watch may not perform. Therefore if it is operating correctly, do not remove it or the train or disturb its adjustment unless urgent.

The power cell has an insulating cup surrounding the sides and part of the negative surface. Make certain it is always in place.

The stem can be withdrawn by depressing on the set lever axle after which the movement will drop out (dial up).

Figure 1 shows the coil block and the circuit block (together called the integrated block) in exploded view. The integrated block must be removed before the balance and bridge are dismantled. To do this, remove the two coil block screws and the two circuit block screws. Next turn the balance 90° counterclockwise so that its magnets are clear of the coil. Holding the balance, slide the integrated block out (Figure 2).

Cleaning and Repairs

After removing the dial and calendar mechanism, the integrated block is taken out and then the balance and bridge. When the integrated block is removed, the second setting lever-balance-brake which is mounted on a boss on the inside of the main plate under the integrated block is removed. Next the retaining pawl, pallet bridge and pallet are taken out in that order. **NOTE:** Remove these only if urgent.

To remove the train, remove the train wheel bridge, sweep second wheel, third wheel, escape wheel. This is followed by the center wheel bridge and center wheel-cannon pinion. Assembling is done in exact reverse. However, when replacing the sweep second wheel, tilt the loose third wheel aside so that its teeth do not contact the sweep second pinion arbor. This will allow both to be positioned in their pivot-holes.

Ultrasonic cleaning is recommended, avoiding liquids containing silicones. Any good watch oil can be used on the jewel pivots and calendar and setting mechanism.

Before replacing the balance assembly, as noted earlier, check the indexing mechanism and the magnetic draw of the pallet. This may be adjusted by bending the banking pins, being careful not to throw the pallet action off-center or breaking a banking pin. Also, the indexing must be checked after the retaining pawl is replaced for all escape teeth. This is done by taking a pointed pegwood (not steel tweezers) and moving the fork from one banking pin to the other, noticing whether an escape tooth is indexed or not. As mentioned earlier, the adjustment of the retaining pawl is critical and most important. This pawl spring must sit in the click wheel with the tolerances

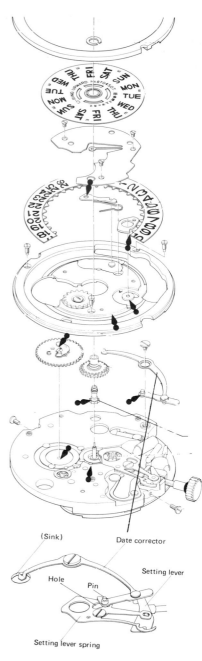

(Sink)   Date corrector

Setting lever

Hole   Pin

Setting lever spring

FIGURE 3

shown in Figure 4. When adjusting for A, Figure 4, do so that a pallet jewel contacts the tooth face and flank of the escape wheel. This is done by twisting the eccentric pin, Figure 5-A. Dimension B, Figure 4 can be adjusted as in Figure 5B and C. Horizontal alignment of the pawl spring is done by bending it close to its pinion point. After each adjustment, test the indexing.

Assemble the balance and bridge with a minimum of endshake to avoid later interference by the coil. Remember to turn the balance 90° counterclockwise as you are inserting the integrated block (Figure 3), having first correctly positioned the balance brake lever. After securing its four screws, inspect its clearance between the upper and lower magnets. At this point it is possible to test the running of the watch by using a (temporary) cell-holding spring to hold the pre-tested cell. Else the electrical circuit can be completed by grounding the (+) temporarily to the balance bridge, bridging the two with a tweezer. With the stem pushed in, the balance should start.

Assemble the dial train and calendar mechanism, making certain that the date corrector is positioned correctly with its bent end in the plate hole and its pivoting tab's pin in the set lever spring slot.

TESTING AND REPAIRS

As in most watches a good amplitude, in this case over 200° is satisfactory. Less, calls for an inspection of the mechanical portions which might interfere. If the mechanical parts are correct, use a damping test. This is done by gently moving the balance as far as it will go. When freeing the balance, it should take ten seconds for it to come to a complete stop.

If the balance stops before ten seconds, the following must be suspect: 1 - Clearance between balance magnets and coil; -adjust endshake or height of coil. 2 - Magnetic draw of pallet; -adjust with banking pins. 3 - Retaining pawl spring pressing on click

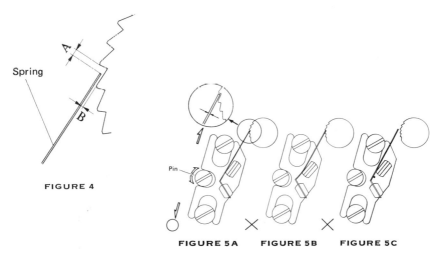

Spring

FIGURE 4

Pin

FIGURE 5A   FIGURE 5B   FIGURE 5C

wheel; -adjust spring's tension. 4 - Sweep second friction spring tension too strong; -adjust. 5 - Train wheel cleanliness or chips clinging to magnets; -clean.

Should the watch still refuse to run or runs unsatisfactory and/ or the damping tests take much over ten seconds, conduct the following: 1 - Ohmmeter continuity test of power supply switch (clutch lever extension and contact pin must have positive contact). 2 - Continuity test of power connection (negative (-) lead piece in cell-well of main plate); -adjust. 3 - Continuity test of integrated block (discussed later.)

Current Consumption

To test current consumption, you will need a 200 to 300 μF condenser across the meter leads. **You may damage the circuit without it.** Set the meter to read microamperes and the condenser connected as shown in Figure 4. A reading of 13 μA is satisfactory (while watch is running). More than 13 μA requires an inspection of the mechanical efficiency previously discussed under Mechanical defects 1-2-3-4-5.

Continuity Checks

Place one end of a meter lead on the (+) surface of the inserted cell and the other end of the meter's wire lead on the balance bridge. With the crown pushed in, the watch should start. Inspect all power connections. If satisfactory proceed to —

Switching Continuity

Set the meter as in Figure 7. The meter should read 0 Ω. Otherwise, inspect contact switch (oil, lint, etc. or poor contact by clutch lever tip). With crown out (contact pin and clutch lever

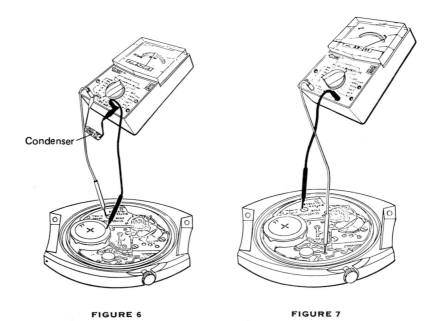

Condenser

FIGURE 6   FIGURE 7

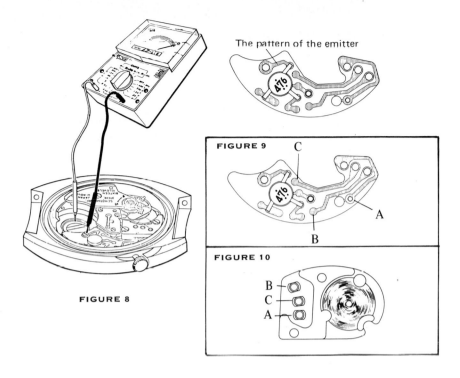

The pattern of the emitter

FIGURE 9

C

A

B

FIGURE 10

B
C
A

FIGURE 8

separated) a reading of over 2M Ω is normal. Under 2M Ω suspect that the integrated block is out of order and must be replaced.

Power Connection Continuity

Set the meter as in Figure 8 (+) lead to circuit block emitter screw; (-) lead to power connector. Zero resistance is normal. Otherwise suspect loose circuit block screw; -fasten these securely.

Integrated Block (see Figure 9)

Resistance (+) to A, (-) to B should exceed 7k Ω . Under 4k Ω indicates that the coil is loose or shorted. Tighten coil block screws, retest. If unsatisfactory, replace coil block. (+) to A, (-) to C = 2k Ω : under 2k Ω , replace circuit block.

Coil Block (Figure 10)

Coil block is removed by three terminal screws on bottom of integrated block. Leads (+) to B and (-) to C should equal between 4.5 to 9k Ω . Over 9k Ω or below 4k Ω indicates a need to replace the coil block. Make certain to secure all screws and clean all contacts.

Marketed by Unisales Time, Sears and various private names. Specifications: 21,600 V.P.H. Power Cell: EPX 77 (1.5V). Power consumption: 16 μ A.

Space allows only a skeletal review of its principles and repair. However, a study of the Seiko El-370 (previous pages), despite differences, has many similar features and will assist in repairs of this watch.

This is both a contact and transistorized watch. As its traditional balance turns counterclockwise, the roller jewel, entering the fork slot makes a contact wire spring complete a circuit. This results in a weak current which trips the transistor and allows the main current to energize a magnetic core coil. This impels a strong bar magnet on the pallet staff. Thus the pallet impels the plain balance in the traditional manner. This occurs only in the counterclockwise direction.

The principle of the retaining pawl, power connection, switching, balance stop, power consumption and other test, if not exactly alike are similar to Seiko El-370.

The movement is removed through the case top after lifting out the crystal. Depressing the tab, Figure 1, allows the stem to be withdrawn. The movement will fall out, dial-down. The dial train and calendar works are simple and easy to dismantle.

Figure 2 shows an exploded view of the electric and integrated block units. Be careful when positioning the lead wires to circuit block connection. It may be resoldered if broken. Also position cautiously the delicate contact point spring. Do not lose the balance bridge shims (if any).

Do not subject the following to machine cleaning: 1 - Circuit block. 2 - Contact point lever and contact point spring (both may be washed in freeon or similar liquid). 3 - Wash jeweled lever separately; remove magnetic chips from its magnet. Follow instructions in Figure 3 for proper assembly of contact point lever and contact spring. Test the indexing of all escape teeth; study Seiko El-370 for adjusting and oiling principles with retaining pawl. Amplitude should be 220°+, stem down. See Seiko El-370 for power consumption tests. Continuity test = 1.3 to 1.5k Ω . Reading of 0 Ω reveals faulty insulation. Repair or replace the coil block.

Continuity Tests (See Figure 4)

With meter set for RX100 Ω : 1 - Place (+) lead to (b), (-) to (a). 1.3 to 1.5k Ω is normal. 2 - Reading of ∞ Ω = disconnected coil; repair or replace. 3 - Reading of 0 Ω = poor insulation. 4 -

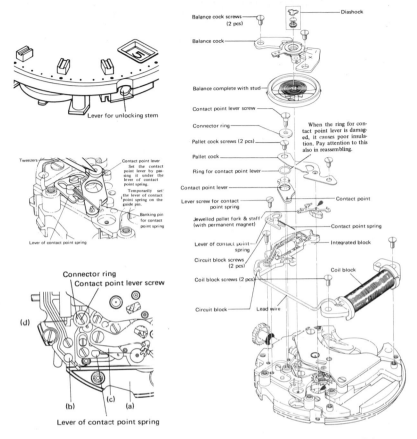

Lever for unlocking stem

Tweezers

Contact point lever
Set the contact point lever by passing it under the lever of contact point spring.

Temporarily set the lever of contact point spring on the guide pin.

Banking pin for contact point spring

Lever of contact point spring

Balance cock screws (2 pcs)

Balance cock

Diashock

Balance complete with stud

Contact point lever screw

Connector ring

Pallet cock screws (2 pcs)

Pallet cock

Ring for contact point lever

Contact point lever

Lever screw for contact point spring

Jewelled pallet fork & staff (with permanent magnet)

Lever of contact point spring

Circuit block screws (2 pcs)

Coil block screws (2 pcs)

Circuit block

Lead wire

When the ring for contact point lever is damaged, it causes poor insulation. Pay attention to this also in reassembling.

Contact point

Contact point spring

Integrated block

Coil block

Connector ring
Contact point lever screw

(d)

(b) (c) (a)

Lever of contact point spring

Recheck coil continuity (detach from movement). If this separated coil shows meter reading = 1.3 to 1.5k Ω , it indicates poor insulation and short-circuited to plate; repair insulation. If separated coil reads 0 Ω , repair or replace coil block.

Continuity Check For Contact Point Pin and Contact Point Spring

Remove balance with cell positioned by temporary holding spring and pallet locked at entrance jewel. Causing contact of spring with contact point should make pallet magnetically jump to other banking. If not, clean, adjust or replace. If (a), and (c), are touched simultaneously and pallet moves, it proves poor contact; clean adjust or replace. If this assembly still fails to move, try touching (d), and (a), simultaneously. If they now move, it indicates poor contact of contact lever point with integrated circuit; tighten the loose contact lever screw and/or clean the connector. If despite all these checks, the pallet fails to jump, unsolder at (b), Figure 4 and replace the circuit block.

TIMEX 69 (6¾ x 8 Ligne)

DIAL SIDE   MOVEMENT SIDE

Pulling out the stem stops the balance and the flow of current. Its 21,600 vibration rate can be checked on any timing machine. Testing the electrical circuit and cell can be done with any multimeter with the usual 20,000 ohms·per volt range.

Figure 1 shows the exploded view and serves as a guide for dismantling and assembly.

To uncase the movement, first remove the energy cell by prying off the cell lid at the point stamped, "Lift Here". The cell will drop out by gravity. After the cell is removed, use a crystal lifter to remove the crystal and reflector ring. There are no screws or levers securing the stem. A sliding sleeve on the stem aids in releasing the stem bracket from the stem. Following Figure 2, remove the stem by pulling it into the set position. Do not mar the crystal seat with the screwdriver but insert the screwdriver behind the sliding sleeve and push the sleeve inward while grasping the movement. This spreads the ears of the stem bracket and the stem can be removed as it is gently withdrawn with a twisting motion. It is important to hold the movement in place during withdrawal. If the sleeve is now in the pendant, it will be necessary to slide the sleeve into position with the tweezers so that the screwdriver can fit behind the sleeve. To replace the stem, hold the movement firmly and press the stem into place to allow its stem pinion to engage the minute wheel teeth.

Remove the movement, noting the locating tabs even during reassembly, otherwise the reflector ring and crystal will not seat properly. Next replace the stem and energy cell using a retaining spring available from Timex. The negative pole (-) must touch the contact spring assembly (4080-exploded view) and the positive pole (+) is grounded to the movement.

To avoid damaging the coil, rotate the balance to the lock position. Carefully remove the shunt bridge, unhooking it from the plate without disturbing the hairspring. **Replace and tighten the shunt bridge screw.**

This is not an electronic watch. A contact spring serves as a switch, allowing current to flow through the drive coil and impart motion to the balance. The contact spring must point exactly to the center of the balance staff and must lie horizontally between the impulse disc and balance. As the length of the contact pin is fixed at the factory, do not try to adjust it.

FIGURE 1

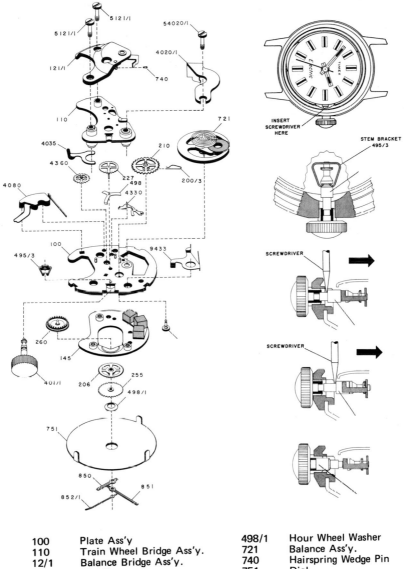

100	Plate Ass'y	498/1	Hour Wheel Washer
110	Train Wheel Bridge Ass'y.	721	Balance Ass'y.
12/1	Balance Bridge Ass'y.	740	Hairspring Wedge Pin
145	Dial Rest	751	Dial
200/2	Friction Pinion	850	Hour Hand
200/3	Friction Spring	851	Minute Hand
206	Center Wheel Ass'y.	852/1	Sweep Second Hand
210	Third Wheel Ass'y.	4020/1	Shunt Bridge
227	Seconds Wheel Ass'y.	4035	Energy Cell Spring
255	Hour Wheel Ass'y.	4080	Contact Spring Ass'y.
260	Minute Wheel Ass'y.	4330	Index Lever Ass'y.
401/1	Setting Stem With Crown	4360	Index Wheel Ass'y.
		5121/1	Balance Bridge Screw
495/3	Stem Bracket	54020/1	Shunt Bridge Screw
498	Friction Washer	9433	Set Spring

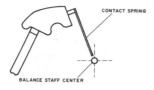

CONTACT SPRING

BALANCE STAFF CENTER

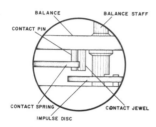

BALANCE — BALANCE STAFF
CONTACT PIN

CONTACT SPRING — CONTACT JEWEL
IMPULSE DISC

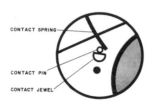

CONTACT SPRING

CONTACT PIN

CONTACT JEWEL

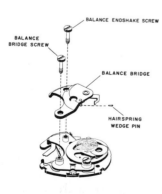

BALANCE ENDSHAKE SCREW

BALANCE
BRIDGE SCREW

BALANCE BRIDGE

HAIRSPRING
WEDGE PIN

The purpose of the contact jewel is to limit the contact between the contact pin and the contact spring so that the flow of electrical energy occurs at the precise position during rotation of the balance.

To remove the balance assembly, un-pin the hairspring and release it from the regulator. Remove the balance endshake screw and next the balance bridge screw. Make sure that the shunt bridge screw is in place before removal of the balance bridge else the train bridge will be disturbed. Now remove the balance.

Remove the shunt bridge screw while holding the train bridge and plate together. This will keep the train wheels from being attracted to the magnets when the train bridge is removed. Like most electrical watches, the pallet banks magnetically and the escape wheel's static position is magnetically maintained. The balance stop mechanism is mechanical, its stop lever catching the lip of the balance's impulse disc.

To clean the movement, it is best to dismantle it only to the point of removing the balance and bridge. The balance should be cleaned separately. Standard cleaning solutions should be used, **avoiding any liquids containing silicones.** Timex uses Elgin M56B oil. Fill the balance cups halfway before inserting the balance. Lubricate; 1 - Impulse pin or fork slot. 2 - Index lever pivots. 3 - Index wheel teeth. 4 - All wheel pivots. 5 - Junction of center wheel and friction washer. 6 - Junction between minute wheel and dial rest. 7 - Grease the stem at stem bracket contact. Don't lubricate contact spring or contact pin on balance.

Balance endshake is governed by the balance bridge screw on the 9 o'clock side. Tightening it reduces endshake but be careful not to damage the balance staff points.

Electrical Checks

Energy cell should check out at 1.5V. A continuity check using an ohmmeter (20,000 ohms per volt) should show a coil resistance value of between 2500 to 4000 Ω.

TIMEX ELECTRONIC
(Model 87)

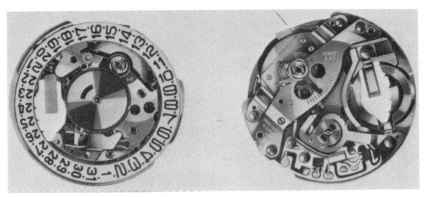

Both dial and movement sides of the model 87 are shown in **Figure 1.**

The transistorized model 87 (calibre 882) is a 13½ ligne calendar watch. The case and crystal interchange with Timex's models 84 and 85.

In the new electronic watch, electromechanical contact has been eliminated. Electrical switching is accomplished by an electronic circuit consisting of two transistors, one capacitor and four resistors. This circuit is connected to the moving coil on the balance by a small hairspring which controls the power supply from the energy cell to the coil on the balance. Figure 1 shows the dial and movement sides of this movement.

Pulling out the crown into the hand-setting position causes a hack mechanism to disconnect the flow of current from the cell as well as stop the watch. In this way the watch can be set to the second. When the crown is pulled out, there is no drain on the energy cell.

The vibration rate of the balance is 21,600, six times a second. The second hand, as in the earlier models, makes one jump each second. Regulation is done through the regulator. An ordinary timing machine will record these pulses.

To check the watch, the usual high-ohm voltmeter of about 20,000 ohms per volt is sufficient. (Most watchmakers already possess such devices for use in everyday electric watch servicing.)

Figure 2 is an exploded view of the movement and the way the parts may be assembled.

Dismantling the Movement

The first step in removing the movement from the case is to take out the energy cell. Avoid damaging the case when opening cell cover. Lift only at the spot on the case back with the arrow and legend "Lift Here."

237

the TIMEX model 87 movement (exploded view)

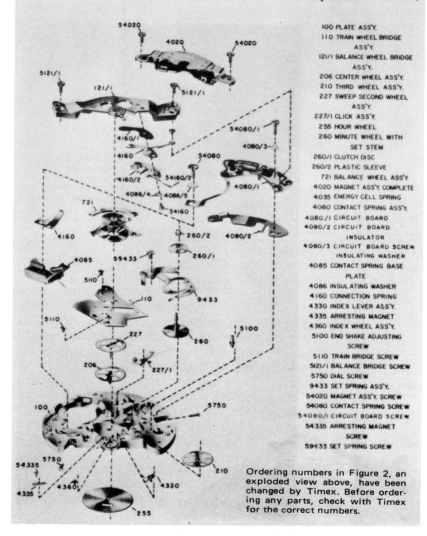

100 PLATE ASS'Y.
110 TRAIN WHEEL BRIDGE
ASS'Y.
121/1 BALANCE WHEEL BRIDGE
ASS'Y.
206 CENTER WHEEL ASS'Y.
210 THIRD WHEEL ASS'Y.
227 SWEEP SECOND WHEEL
ASS'Y.
227/1 CLICK ASS'Y.
255 HOUR WHEEL
260 MINUTE WHEEL WITH
SET STEM
260/1 CLUTCH DISC
260/2 PLASTIC SLEEVE
721 BALANCE WHEEL ASS'Y.
4020 MAGNET ASS'Y. COMPLETE
4035 ENERGY CELL SPRING
4080 CONTACT SPRING ASS'Y.
4080/1 CIRCUIT BOARD
4080/2 CIRCUIT BOARD
INSULATOR
4080/3 CIRCUIT BOARD SCREW
INSULATING WASHER
4085 CONTACT SPRING BASE
PLATE
4086 INSULATING WASHER
4160 CONNECTION SPRING
4330 INDEX LEVER ASS'Y.
4335 ARRESTING MAGNET
4360 INDEX WHEEL ASS'Y.
5100 END SHAKE ADJUSTING
SCREW
5110 TRAIN BRIDGE SCREW
5121/1 BALANCE BRIDGE SCREW
5750 DIAL SCREW
9433 SET SPRING ASS'Y.
54020 MAGNET ASS'Y. SCREW
54080 CONTACT SPRING SCREW
54080/1 CIRCUIT BOARD SCREW
54335 ARRESTING MAGNET
SCREW
59433 SET SPRING SCREW

Ordering numbers in Figure 2, an exploded view above, have been changed by Timex. Before ordering any parts, check with Timex for the correct numbers.

After removing the cell (Figure 3), check its voltage. If it has less than 1.5 volts or if you know it has been in service for longer than a year, replace it. Avoid short-circuiting the cell by carelessly moving tweezers across the poles or through metallic contacts across these poles.

Next, remove the crystal using a crystal lifter. The movement can now be removed through the front of the case. Note the locating notch in the bezel seat, A, and the corresponding key on the balance bridge, B.

Do not attempt to remove the case back; it is fixed permanently to the case! The crown set wheel remains with the case back. An automatic coupling connects the wheel with the stem when the movement is returned to the case.

Should the crown set wheel require removal, however, use the following procedure (Figure 4). Lift the crown set wheel to the "stop" position. Next, with the tips of the tweezers spread open the retaining spring and push the crown set wheel down through the rear of the case. If necessary, the retaining spring and gasket can then be removed.

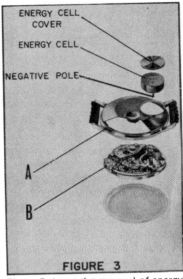

FIGURE 3

Figure 3 shows the removal of energy cell.

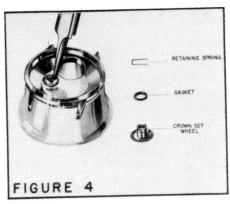

FIGURE 4

In Figure 4 the procedure for removing the crown set wheel is illustrated. Figure 5 shows the assembly of the energy cell retaining spring. Screws A and B must be loosened.

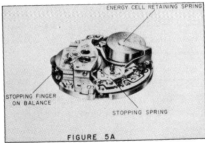

FIGURE 5A

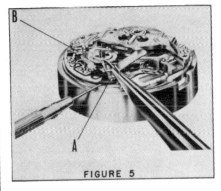

FIGURE 5

In Figure 5A the energy cell retaining spring is pressing the stopping spring and permitting the balance to turn freely.

To examine the functioning of the movement, place it on a movement block and clamp the cell in place with an energy cell retaining spring. This retaining spring is available on request from the Timex Material Sales Division.

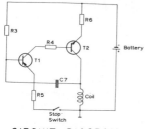

CIRCUIT DIAGRAM

FIGURE 6

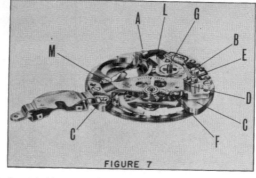

FIGURE 7

Figure 6 shows the change from electrical to mechanical impulses. To rotate the magnet system and shunt bridge out of position, as shown in Figure 7, remove screw C.

To assemble the energy cell retaining spring, loosen screws A and B, Figure 5. Lift the switch insulation with a screwdriver and insert the energy cell retaining spring between the switch insulation and the hand setting spring. Then tighten the screws again. One end of the energy cell retaining spring depresses the stopping spring fixed to the movement and allows the balance to turn freely, as in Figure 5A.

Electrical System

The negative pole of the energy cell must contact the connection spring (4160 in exploded view). Current from the negative pole flows through the connection spring to the connection yoke of the electronic circuit. These parts are insulated from the rest of the movement. The positive pole of the energy cell touches the energy cell retaining spring, and energy flows to the plate, 100.

Never cause a metallic connection between the insulated and uninsulated parts of the movement. The resulting shortcircuit will shorten the life of the cell.

As shown in Figure 6, the electrical impulses of the electronic circuit are changed to mechanical driving impulses for the balance in the same manner as in the Timex model 84. The impulse current flows through the balance drive coil, and the magnetic south pole of the coil is attracted by the north pole and repulsed by the south pole of the permanent magnet system. The electronic circuit is triggered by the voltage induced in the balance coil when it is moving through the permanent magnet system.

The permanent magnet system with the shunt bridge can be rotated out of position so that the balance wheel and hairspring are visible. To do this, remove one screw, C (Figure 7). If desired, this assembly may be completely removed by taking out both screws, C.

After removing the permanent magnet from the movement, the balance bridge and balance can be dislodged. Screw D adjusts endshake of the balance and is fixed in place with epoxy. Before disassembling the balance bridge, screw E, which joins the electronic circuit to the balance bridge, must be disconnected from the balance bridge.

Furthermore, the bronze hairspring and stud must be removed from the bridge by loosening screw F. To separate the hairspring stud from the bridge, press it down out of the balance bridge. An insulating washer, located beneath the screw, holds the bronze hairspring clamp block. Be certain that the washer is in place during the re-assembly; otherwise, a shortcircuit will occur.

The crown set wheel stem, G, is also the staff of the minute wheel. It connects to the crown set wheel on the case back through the clutch device.

In Figure 8 the crown set wheel is depressed into its running position. The clutch disc is not engaged with the stem, and the

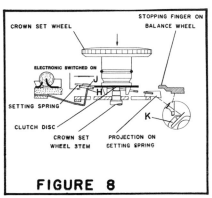

FIGURE 8

Figure 8 shows the running position of the watch with the crown set wheel depressed.

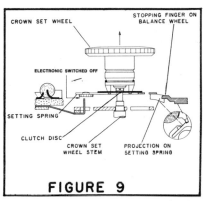

FIGURE 9

In Figure 9 the crown set wheel is in the set position. The electronic circuit is interrupted, and the hands can be set.

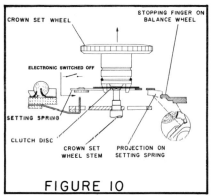

FIGURE 10

Figure 10 shows the procedure to adjust the setting spring. The crown set wheel is up, and the clutch disengages from the stem.

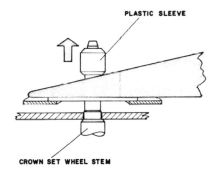

Figure 11 shows the plastic sleeve being lifted from the stem with tweezers.

setting spring is pressed in. In this position the projection on the setting spring is kept out of engagement with the stopping finger of the balance wheel. The nose, H, of the stop switch must touch the rivet, J, of the setting spring.

In Figure 9 the crown set wheel is in the set position. The clutch disc now engages with the square portion of the stem and couples the stem and crown set wheel so the hands can be set. This position of the crown set wheel also allows the setting spring to move upwards and butt against the stopping finger on the balance wheel. The nose, H, of the stop switch must be clear of the rivet, J, of the setting spring, thus interrupting the starting current of the electronic circuit.

Adjusting the Setting Spring

Should the setting spring require adjustment, use the following procedure. Move the crown set wheel upwards so that the clutch disc just disengages from the square part of the set stem (Figure 10). The clutch disc will rest against the bottom of the square portion of the stem. In this position the projection on the setting spring must contact the stopping finger on the balance wheel by the amount shown in Figure 10.

When the crown set wheel is pulled into the set position (Figure 9), the stopping finger on the balance wheel must fully contact the projection on the setting spring. For this adjustment, bend the setting spring in the area marked K. The nose, H, of the stop switch must be clear of the rivet, J, on the setting spring by at least a half to one and a half times the thickness of the setting spring. If necessary, adjust this clearance by bending the setting spring in area L, Figure 7.

To **remove the clutch** mechanism from the movement, first lift the plastic sleeve from the stem with tweezers, as shown in Figure 11. Next, remove the clutch disc (part 260/1). Then, take off screw A and the setting spring (Figure 12).

The electronic circuitry can now be taken off by removing screws B and M. Screws at positions B and M have insulating

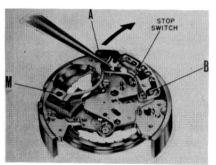

FIGURE 12

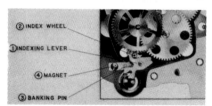

FIGURE 13

Figure 12 illustrates the removal of the electronic module. Screws B and M must be taken off. The circuit base is lifted until the stop switch clears the train bridge. In Figure 13 the gear train is exposed. The balance wheel is turning counterclockwise.

washers which must be replaced during reassembly; otherwise, a shortcircuit will occur. The screws at position M should also be removed.

Lift the circuit base, as shown in Figure 12, turning it in the direction of the arrow until the stop switch clears the train bridge. Take care that the stop switch does not become damaged.

Gear Train

Figures 13 and 14 show the gear train exposed, that is, with the train bridge removed. The action of the gear train is as follows:

242

In Figure 13, the balance wheel turns counterclockwise, which moves the indexing lever (1) to the left. The lever contains a steel D-shaped pin which advances the index wheel (2) forward one tooth. After moving the index wheel forward, the index lever comes to rest against the banking pin (3). The tip of one tooth on the index wheel is fixed in position by the magnet (4).

Since the index wheel is magnetically fixed in position, the steel D-shaped pin on the index lever cannot move of its own accord out of its position between the teeth of the index wheel.

When the balance wheel turns clockwise, as in Figure 14, it moves the index lever to the right. The steel D-shaped pin will now move the index wheel backwards slightly until the pin clears the tooth of the index wheel. The index lever comes to rest against the banking pin and is held by the attraction between the magnet and the D-shaped pin.

The moment the steel D-shaped pin clears the index wheel, the attraction of the arresting magnet pulls the wheel back to its original position. There, it is set for another one-tooth advancement during the next counterclockwise rotation of the balance.

When the index wheel has moved forward three teeth, one tooth of the two-toothed pinion fixed to the index wheel engages the sweep second wheel and rotates it forward one tooth. This one-tooth rotation of the sweep second wheel, aided by the click (5), allows the one-second "jump" of the sweep second hand.

The safety finger (6) insures that no more than one tooth of the sweep second wheel will index at a time. The click spring must be locked as shown in the illustration. Pre-tension of the click spring should be two to two-and-a-half times the diameter of the locking pin.

The remainder of the gear train functions in the normal manner, but, as in all battery-powered watches, the pinions drive the wheels. The sweep second wheel pinion in this watch drives the third wheel. The third wheel pinion, in turn, rotates the center wheel. The center wheel carries the minute hand, and the teeth of the center wheel mesh with the minute wheel. The minute wheel staff projects through to the dial side and carries the minute pinion.

The third wheel assembly (Figure 15) provides the dial train friction. A friction washer is placed between the third wheel pinion and the third wheel. It is important to carefully lubricate this piece after cleaning.

The arresting magnet may be removed to check the train (Figure 16). While removing the magnet, the index lever must be in the position shown in Figure 13. When assembling the hands, the sweep second wheel assembly must be supported at the pivot to avoid damage.

Reassembling the Watch

To assemble, position the electronic circuit above the pin, P, as shown in Figure 17. Push the stop switch down to a level slightly below the nose of the train bridge, R. Holding the stop switch down, move the circuit to its final position over pin P.

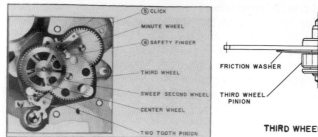
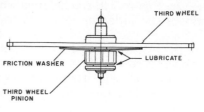

THIRD WHEEL ASSEMBLY

In Figure 14 (left) the balance wheel turns clockwise. When the index wheel moves forward three teeth, the sweep second hand jumps one second. Figure 15 (right) displays the third wheel assembly which provides the dial train friction.

This action will lock the switch into position below the nose of the train bridge, R. Be certain that the stop switch insulator, which is part of the circuit board, is in its proper position between the nose of the bridge, R, and the stop switch.

The stop switch is insulated from the bridge. Use care to avoid damaging the stop switch. Now assemble the setting spring and the screws holding the circuit board.

Use the disassembly procedure as a guide for further reassembly. When replacing the movement in the case, pull the crown set wheel out into the set position to ease entry of the setting stem into the crown set wheel.

Cleaning, Oiling and Timing

The movement, including the electronic circuit, may be cleaned in the usual method using normal commercial cleaning and rinsing solutions. Do not use perchlorethylene or similar hydrocarbons on these watches.

The balance must be cleaned separately to prevent damage to the coil. Do not clean the energy cell with any liquid. If necessary, wipe it with a dry, clean cloth only.

After cleaning, any particles adhering to the magnet should be carefully removed before assembly. A piece of Scotch tape or "Rodico" rolled into a point will remove particles which adhere to the magnet, etc. Do not use this process after the movement is assembled as there is danger of severing the lead wires of the balance coil.

The other parts of the movement must be free of particles, especially steel or nickel which would be drawn to the magnet. Needless to say, the watch should not be demagnetized.

Re-oil the movement in the normal manner using only high grade watch oils. The oil used in factory assembly of these watches is Elgin M56b. Under no circumstances should oil or grease containing silicone be used. This is a good practice to follow on all battery-driven watches.

Certain points require lubrication: a. The jewel bearings and pivots of the train wheels and balance. b. The minute wheel and set stem bearing surfaces. c. The steel D-shaped pin on the index lever. d. The surface of the click which rests against the sweep

244

Figure 16 shows the arresting magnet which is removed to check the train. Index lever must be in the position shown in Figure 13 when the magnet is being removed.

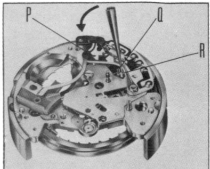

Pin P in Figure 17 must be pushed down below the nose of the train bridge, R, to begin reassembling the watch.

second wheel. e. The third wheel assembly as shown in Figure 15. f. The pipe of the crown set wheel so that the lubricant will seep down to the rubber water-proofing gasket which surrounds the pipe.

Never lubricate the connection point between the stop switch and the setting spring.

The best performance of the Timex electronic is achieved if the hairspring does not vibrate between the pin and the regulator key. The outside edge of the hairspring should be in light permanent contact with the inside edge of the regulator key. Make sure that both hairsprings have good clearance to all other movement parts, including the balance bridge and upper shunt of the driving magnet.

Checking the Circuit

Actually, there is little to check on this electronic module. Since there are no electro-mechanical contacts, no adjustments can or need be made. The transistorized circuit electronically supplies the impulses to the balance.

If the watch does not operate even though all the mechanical parts have been checked according to the instructions, check the energy cell to see whether it has the specified 1.5 voltage. If it does not and the cell has been installed recently, then see whether you have omitted any insulating washers which would cause a short circuit and drain the energy cell. It is also possible that faulty assembly has caused a short circuit.

If everything checks out and the watch still does not function, then suspect the electronic module. This entire unit should then be replaced. It is easily removed, as shown in Figure 12. Make sure the insulating washers for screws B and M are correctly replaced.

Working with the model 87, this writer has found regulation is possible to within five seconds daily.